I Spy with
BABAR
at the seaside

MADCAP

Hurrah! It's holiday time at last. Babar and

his family are going to stay at the seaside on

a tropical 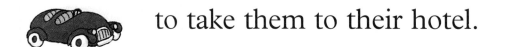 .

First, they travel on an  . When

they arrive at the airport, Babar hires a

to take them to their hotel.

As they drive along they see lots of

growing by the side of the road.

It's their first day on the beach. The

is shining and there is no cloud in the sky.

The children can hardly wait to put on their

 and blow up their

Babar fixes the firmly in the

sand so that it won't blow over.

It really is a beautiful day!

The green is flying to show that it is safe to go into the water. Isabelle can't swim very well, so she uses a  which looks like a duck.

Arthur puts on his  and his and sets off to do some underwater exploring.

Oh dear! He forgets to put on the snorkle and swallows a big mouthful of salty sea water.

There are all sorts of wonderful and

beautiful things to discover under the sea.

Arthur meets lots of brightly coloured 13

and an  which runs away, leaving

a cloud of black ink behind it.

The  is frightened of Arthur and

hides behind some 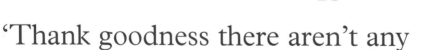 .

6

'Thank goodness there aren't any

dangerous, big sharks,' thinks Arthur.

Isabelle is tired of swimming and being

splashed by the  . She lies down

on her  , and puts on her

and her sunglasses.

She looks so pretty that the  , who

is sunbathing on the rocks, can't believe his

eyes. He thinks Isabelle must be a famous

film-star.

19

Pom is building a  . He mixes

water and sand together in a

to make the towers.

Then he takes his  and digs a moat

all around the sandcastle. To finish, he puts

two down to guard the

drawbridge. Well done, Pom! Your

sandcastle is nearly as grand as Babar's

palace.

Flora and Zephir take their  and

go to see what they can find in the rock

pools.

Flora sees a with five arms.

Zephir finds a . But it is cross

because its hiding place has been

discovered.

Careful, Zephir. The crab has very sharp

 and you might get hurt.

Meanwhile, Arthur enjoys playing with his

The   re very puzzled when they

see the kite. They fly around to look at this

strange-looking bird!

Celeste settles down on a   and

covers herself with sun cream.   Everyone is

busy, so she can enjoy a few moments of

peace and finish reading her   .

Now, what can Babar be up to? There he is,

on his  holding his

carefully in front of him.

Th have been pulled out of the

water and the is empty.

Everything is perfectly still and quiet.

Do you think Babar is having a little sleep?

Night falls and the sky gets very dark, so

Arthur lights a  on the beach.

Suddenly, a  leaps out of the

waves. 'He must have come to say

goodnight,' says Zephir. 'What a pity I

didn't have my ready to take his

photograph.'

'A photo of the  would be good,'

says Babar.

Zephir's photos will make a perfect souvenir

of their seaside holiday.

Babar Characters™ and © 1999 Laurent de Brunhoff
Licensed by Nelvana Limited and The Clifford Ross Company Ltd
First published by Hachette Livre
Artwork adapted by Jean-Claude Gilbert
from the original characters created by Jean and Laurent de Brunhoff
Text: Agathe Baudet
English adaptation: Michèle Brown

Printed and bound in Italy
ISBN: 0 233 99637 0

Also available in this series:

I spy with Babar in the country

I spy with Babar on the farm

Other **BABAR** titles available in Madcap

ISBN 0 233 99395 9
£7.99

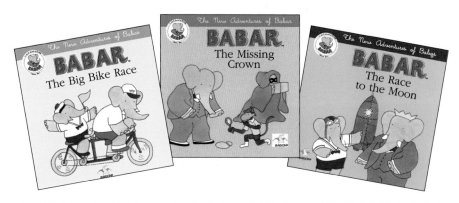

ISBN 0 233 99439 4   ISBN 0 233 99441 6   ISBN 0 233 99440 8
£2.99   £2.99   £2.99

All these titles are available and can be bought at your local bookshop,
or ordered direct from Littlehampton Book Services,
10-14 Eldon Way, Littlehampton, West Sussex, BN17 7HE
Tel: 01903 721596 Fax: 01903 828802

EDEXCEL A-LEVEL RELIGIOUS STUDIES

PAPER 3 NEW TESTAMENT STUDIES

6   CHALLENGES & ETHICAL LIVING

CII00841338

Published independently by Tinderspark Press
© Jonathan Rowe 2018
www.philosophydungeon.weebly.com

The purchaser of this book is subject to the condition that he/she shall in no way resell it, nor any part of it, nor make copies of it to distribute freely.
All illustrations in this book are Creative Commons. The cover illustration is stained glass from Church of Saint-Eutrope in Clermont-Ferrand. Biblical quotations are from the New International Version UK (NIV-UK).
The author is not affiliated with the Edexcel Exam Board and makes no claim to represent Edexcel's policies, standards or practices.

CONTENTS

ABOUT THIS BOOK

This book offers advice for teachers and students approaching Year 2 of Edexcel A-Level Religious Studies, Paper 3 (New Testament Studies). It concentrates on **Topic 6 (Scientific & historical-critical challenges, ethical living and the works of scholars)**.

Together with this one, these books cover Year2 of the A-Level.

4   Ways of interpreting the Scripture

5   Texts and interpretation: the Kingdom of God, conflict, the death and resurrection of Jesus

The **New Testament Year 2 Study Guide** brings all 3 of these books together in one volume. These three study guides are summarised in note format in **Revision Guide 2**, which also includes revision exercises, quizzes and exam-style questions for AS and A-Level but doesn't have the sort of detailed explanations that are in the study guides.

The remaining books cover the topics in Year 1 of the A-Level and/or the AS course. The other Year 1 topics are:

1   Social, historical and religious context of the New Testament

2   Texts & interpretation of the Person of Jesus

3   Interpreting the text and issues of relationship, purpose & authorship

The **New Testament AS/Year 1 Study Guide** brings all 3 of these books together in one volume. These three study guides are also summarised in note format in **Revision Guide 1**, but there is also **Revision Guide 3** which covers all 6 study guides in note format and has exam questions for the entire A-Level (but not AS).

> *Text that is indented and shaded like this is a quotation from a scholar or from the Bible. Candidates should use some of these quotations in their exam responses.*

Text in this typeface and boxed represents the author's comments, observations and reflections. Such texts are not intended to guide candidates in writing exam answers. In other words, quote the Gospels or quote Aristotle but don't quote ME.

SCIENTIFIC & HISTORICAL-CRITICAL CHALLENGES, ETHICAL LIVING AND THE WORKS OF SCHOLARS

What's this topic about?

What are the implications of the Resurrections? Can modern people still believe in it as a miraculous event or must it be viewed symbolically? What are the implications for ethical living in a multi-faith society?

SCIENTIFIC & HISTORICAL-CRITICAL CHALLENGES

This topic looks at the death and resurrection of Jesus in modern scholarship, including Enlightenment challenges to the resurrection as a miracle and views of it as a fiction, a myth or a subjective experience. There are no key scholars but **Frank Morison** and **Ian Wilson** feature in the Anthology.

HOW SHOULD WE LIVE?

This topic covers Jesus' **sermon on the plain** in Luke's Gospel and 3 Parables (**Good Samaritan, Lost Sheep//Coin/Son** and **Rich Man & Lazarus**) as well as Jesus' teachings in **relation to Judaism**. Key scholars are **I. Howard Marshall** and (*we suppose*) **Frank J. Matera**.

Before you go any further...

... there are some things you need to know.

THE RESURRECTION IN THE GOSPELS

The Resurrection is Jesus being raised from the dead. The Gospels provide other examples of persons being raised from the dead (the son of the widow of Nain in **Luke 7: 11-15**, Jairus' daughter in **Luke 8: 41-55**, Lazarus in **John 11: 1-44** and *many holy people who had died* when Jesus is crucified in **Matthew 27: 50-53**). However, these are not 'resurrections'. These people are *restored* to life but to the old life that they had before, which will inevitably end again in death. The Resurrection is Jesus being raised to a NEW KIND OF LIFE.

- It is a life **not restricted by the laws of nature** (the Risen Jesus can appear and disappear)
- It is a **physical life** (the Gospels describe the Risen Jesus being touched and eating food)
- It is a life in a **different sort of body** (the Risen Jesus is not always recognised, even by people who knew him well, until he does or says something distinctive)
- It is a life that **continues in a new heavenly reality** (the Risen Jesus ascends into Heaven, after which the Resurrection-appearances stop)

It is worth examining how each Gospel presents the Resurrection.

The Resurrection in Mark

According to the theory of **Markan Priority** (c.f. **Topic 3.1**), Mark is the earliest Gospel so Mark's description of the Resurrection holds particular interest. However, the earliest surviving texts of Mark's Gospel end at **Mark 16: 8** with the women discovering the empty tomb, receiving a message from a mysterious young man (or angel) and fleeing in fear: "*they said nothing to anyone, because they were afraid.*"

- Some scholars think that the women did in fact go to the Eleven Disciples (eleven since the departure of Judas the betrayer) and tell them about the empty tomb; they just *said nothing to anyone* on the way back from the tomb. Logically, since Mark narrates what the women experienced, they **must** have told someone.
- Other scholars think Mark deliberately ends the Gospel here in this unsatisfactory way in order to encourage the reader to do what the women failed to do: to go out a bear witness to the Resurrection themselves. This interpretation is linked to a **literary interpretation of Scripture** (c.f. **Topic 4**), because Mark ends his Gospel they way he does, not to describe the facts of what happened, but to produce an emotional and imaginative effect on his readers.

Later, two endings were added on to Mark's Gospel. The 'shorter ending' reads like this:

> *Then they quickly reported all these instructions to those around Peter. After this, Jesus himself also sent out through them from east to west the sacred and imperishable proclamation of eternal salvation. Amen.*

This ending clears up the facts that the women **did** tell **Peter** and the other Disciples about the empty tomb and it emphasises the Resurrection is a message for everyone in the world, not just Jews. However, it still doesn't include any Resurrection appearances.

The 'longer ending' features in modern Bibles as **Mark 16: 9-20** and seems to have been added by the end of the 2nd century, if not earlier. It contains four episodes:

1. Jesus appears to **Mary Magdalene** (the leader of the group of women) but no one believes her.
2. Jesus appears *in a different form* to two unnamed disciples *while they were walking in the country*. This links to the passage in **Luke** describing the Risen Jesus' appearance **on the road to Emmaus** (*c.f.* **Topic 5**). Unlike in **Luke**'s version, these disciples are not believed either.
3. Jesus appears to the Eleven while they are eating (perhaps a reference to the Christian celebration of the **Eucharist**), criticises their lack of faith and commissions them to spread the word of his teachings and Resurrection.
4. Finally, Jesus ascends into Heaven.

This ending also emphasises the Resurrection being a message for the whole world and maintains a typical Markan theme of the Disciples lacking faith. It also preserves the tradition that Mary Magdalene was the first witness to the Resurrection.

The Resurrection in Matthew

According to **Source Criticism** (*c.f.* **Topic 3**), Matthew's Gospel drew heavily on Mark's account, supplementing it with extra details from "**Q**" and perhaps other sources. Matthew closely follows the story from the 'longer ending' to Mark:

1. The women (including **Mary Magdalene**) are the first to encounter the Risen Jesus, meeting him on the way back from the empty tomb
2. The Eleven Disciples meet the Risen Jesus in Galilee and, once again, *some doubted* but Jesus gives them the 'Great Commission' to *go and make disciples of all the nations* (i.e. the Gentiles). The Ascension is *not* described.

Matthew also includes a detail missing from the other Gospels that Roman soldiers were set to guard the tomb but were knocked unconscious by an angel. The solders are bribed by the Jewish leaders to spread a false story that the Disciples stole Jesus' body, a story *"which has been widely circulated among the Jews to this very day"* according to **Matthew 28: 15**.

The Resurrection in Luke

You covered this account in depth in **Topic 6.3 (Crucifixion & Resurrection in Luke)**. These are the main points:

1. The women do *not* encounter the Risen Jesus
2. Jesus appears to two disciples **on the road to Emmaus** but they do not recognise him until he breaks bread with them
3. Luke claims (but does not describe) **Peter** as being the first to meet the Risen Jesus.
4. The Eleven Disciples think the Risen Jesus is a ghost but he invites them to touch him and he eats food in front of them
5. The Ascension is described but not the commission to take the message to the Gentiles (although Luke does describe this in his second volume, the **Book of Acts**).

The Resurrection in John

As you would expect, **John**'s account is different from the Synoptic Gospels but includes some striking similarities:

1. **Mary Magdalene** is the first to encounter the Risen Jesus; at first she does not recognise him (and takes him to be the gardener outside the tomb) but she does recognise him when he calls her by name
2. Jesus next appears to the Eleven Disciples and instructs them to touch his hands and feet
3. Jesus appears again when **'Doubting' Thomas** is present and Thomas touches the nail wounds in Jesus' hands and the spear wound in his side

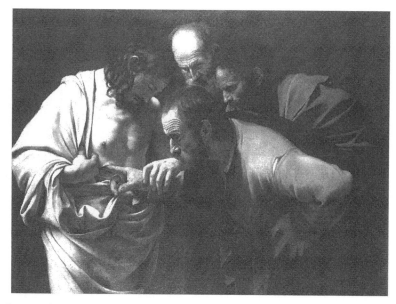

Doubting Thomas investigates Jesus' wounds in Caravaggio's painting of John 20: 24-29

John's Gospel seems to end at **John 20: 31** in its original form, but **John 31** describes more Resurrection appearances:

4. The Disciples meet Jesus in Galilee while they are fishing; they do not recognise him at first but when they do they land a miraculous catch of fish (with the 153 fish perhaps **symbolising** the members of the **Johannine Community**). Jesus reinstates **Peter** as the leader of the Disciples. There is no Ascension scene but it is implied because Jesus talks about a period of delay *"until I return"* (meaning *Parousia* or the 'Second Coming').

The Resurrection according to Paul

Paul's **epistles** (letters) make up 28% of the New Testament. Paul was not one of Jesus' original Disciples: he was a **Pharisee** who persecuted the first Christians. However, he converted to Christianity after a vision of the Risen Christ. He passes on his understanding of the Resurrection as he claims to have *received it* from others:

> *he appeared to Cephas* [i.e. Peter] *and then to the Twelve. After that, he appeared to more than five hundred of the brothers and sisters at the same time* – **1 Corinthians 15: 5-6**

Paul's account makes no mention of the women (or the empty tomb, for that matter) and agrees with Luke in that Cephas/Peter was the first witness to the Resurrection.

Remember that Paul wrote in the 50s CE when Christianity was just beginning; his account is 10-15 years earlier than Mark and 30 years earlier than Matthew or Luke.

Paul also describes his **own** Resurrection experience, which is both similar to and different from the other Disciples.

Paul (at that time named Saul) was a servant of the High Priest in Jerusalem who assisted in the stoning to death of Stephen, the first Christian martyr.

Around 33-36 CE, Saul travelled to Damascus to persecute the Christian community there, but has a dramatic encounter on the road:

> *I saw a light from heaven, brighter than the sun, blazing around me and my companions. We all fell to the ground, and I heard a voice saying to me in Aramaic, 'Saul, Saul, why do you persecute me?'* **– Acts 26: 13-14**

Saul asks who is speaking to him and hears the reply: *"I am Jesus, whom you are persecuting."*

Paul is struck blind by this **numinous religious experience** (termed a CHRISTOPHANY, an encounter with the Risen Christ), Saul converts to Christianity, changes his name to Paul and becomes an enthusiastic missionary for the very faith he had been persecuting. When Paul converts, his blindness disappears.

Evaluating the Resurrection Accounts

There are striking DISSIMILARITIES between these accounts:

- Who is first to encounter the Risen Jesus? **Mark** (in the 'longer version'), **Matthew** and **John** claim it is the women, specifically **Mary Magdalene**; **Luke** and **Paul** claim it is **Peter**
- Where do the Resurrection appearances take place? **Mark** implies and **Matthew** explicitly states they are in Galilee; **Luke** is clear that they are in and around Jerusalem; **John** describes Jerusalem **and** Galilee
- When do the Resurrection appearances end? **Mark** (in the 'longer version') and **Luke** describe the Ascension; **Matthew** and **John** do not

Some critics emphasize these dissimilarities to cast doubt on the Resurrection. However **E.P Saunders** points out that the accounts possess many of the confusions of actual eyewitnesses to dramatic events (like disasters); if the Resurrection was a hoax created by the disciples, you would **expect** the accounts to be much more consistent. Furthermore, there are basic SIMILARITIES between the accounts:

- Jesus' body disappears. The women are the first witnesses to the empty tomb but are not believed
- The Risen Jesus is not always recognised at first: this happens in **Luke** and in **John** (twice: first for **Mary Magdalene** and then for the Eleven Disciples)
- **Luke** describes the mystical encounter **on the road to Emmaus** and **Mark** (in the 'longer version') seems to refer to this too
- Jesus appears to the Eleven Disciples; **Luke** and **John** both describe their disbelief and Jesus offers himself to them to be touched and eats food
- Jesus gives the Disciples a 'commission' to preach to the Gentiles; in **Mark** and **Matthew** this is explicit; **Luke** makes it explicit in his sequel, the **Book of Acts**; in **John** it is only implied

There are also AMBIGUITIES (details that can be interpreted in different ways):

- Some of the encounters seem to be very **symbolic** and may be **allegories** for encountering Christ in the Eucharist celebration (i.e. a **mystical** experience) rather than literal descriptions of meetings (e.g. the **road to Emmaus**)
- The encounters, especially **Paul**'s Christophany, seem more like **visions** – except that **Luke** and **John** both go out of their way to establish that the Risen Jesus is physical
- The time frame is very unclear and almost dream-like: **Luke** presents the encounters as all happening on the same day but in **Acts 1: 3** he states that the appearances happened over 40 days; **Matthew** and **John** flash from Jerusalem to Galilee; **Mark** is completely non-specific about where and when the encounters take place.

These ambiguities lead some scholars to suppose that the Gospel accounts are not *supposed* to be interpreted **literally**. If this is the case, then the original readers of the Gospels might have understood that these descriptions to be **allegories**. Liberal scholars today interpret the Resurrection in this way, but conservative (and especially fundamentalist) Christians insist on a literal interpretation and often quote **Paul** in support:

> *if Christ has not been raised, our preaching is useless and so is your faith* – **1 Corinthians 15: 14**

Whatever ambiguities might be present in the Gospels, Paul is the earliest Christian commentator on the Resurrection and seems to treat it as a historical event, not an allegory.

However, Paul's own Christophany is not an encounter with the physically resurrected Christ. It is more like a **vision** (although Paul's companions seem to experience it too). This leads some scholars to wonder if Paul (who never mentions the empty tomb) really believed in a physical, bodily Resurrection of Jesus.

> *How did Christianity begin: with an allegory about Jesus' message surviving his death, a vision of the dead Jesus or Jesus rising back to physical life?*

BELIEF & DISBELIEF IN THE GOSPELS

It is significant that the Gospels do **not** present the response to the Resurrection as being immediate belief, even when the Risen Jesus physically appears.

- The Disciples disbelieve the women's testimony
- The Disciples think Jesus is a ghost at first (e.g. in **Luke** and **John**)
- **Paul**'s letter to the **Corinthians** shows that some of them doubted the Resurrection, which is why he argues that it is central to Christian faith

The episodes where some disciples recognise the Risen Jesus but others don't might represent the different reactions of belief and disbelief among Jesus' followers.

However, the reaction of the disciples is important because it shows they were not gullible fools or naturally inclined to believe people could come back from the dead.

> *that Jesus of Nazareth was raised from the dead was just as controversial nineteen hundred years ago as it is today*– **N.T. Wright**

The Priestly Plot in Matthew

Matthew 28: 11-15 describes how the Jewish leaders bribe the Roman soldiers to spread the story that the disciples stole Jesus' body to fake the Resurrection. This shows that there were disbelievers making these claims at the time Matthew was writing (around 85 CE perhaps).

> *Who to believe? It's interesting (and a bit sad) that there was a problem with 'Fake News' two thousand years ago, just like today*

However, the important point is that, right from the beginning of the Christian religion, there were doubts about the Resurrection and people were suggesting NATURALISTIC (non-supernatural) explanations for what had happened.

Hellenic vs Jewish conceptions

The Gentiles in the **Hellenic culture** of the Roman Empire mostly followed a DUALIST philosophy: they believed body and spirit were separate, that bodies were mortal and died but spirits could be immortal and might live on without the body. For people like this, it would be understandable (although still surprising) if Jesus returned from the dead as a spirit.

> *Some Gentiles interpreted the Resurrection that way. Paul's letter to the Corinthians seems to address Gentile converts who believed in a 'spiritual' rather than a physical Resurrection. The passages in Luke and John where the Disciples touch Jesus oppose this belief.*

Most 1st century Jews did **not** follow a dualist philosophy: they believed body and soul were one. The **Pharisees** believed in a general resurrection of the dead at the end of time but the **Sadducees** believed there would be no resurrection of the dead. The idea of **one particular person** being raised from the dead by God would not have fitted in with their beliefs either.

Therefore, from a philosophical standpoint, the Resurrection of Jesus would be difficult for 1st century Gentiles AND Jews to accept; perhaps just as difficult as for 21st century secular people.

Seeing is *not* Believing

A feature of the Gospel accounts is that the disciples do not believe in the Resurrection **even when** they encounter the Risen Jesus.

> *When they saw him, they worshiped him; but some doubted* – **Matthew 28: 17**

Matthew's Gospel doesn't explain why *some doubted* but we can assume that these disciples suspected this was a hallucination or a hoax. **Luke** gives more detail:

> *They were startled and frightened, thinking they saw a ghost* – **Luke 24: 37**

Luke's Gospel clarifies that people only believe fully in the Resurrection when they correctly understand the Scriptures. For example, the Risen Jesus says:

> *Everything must be fulfilled that is written about me in the Law of Moses* [i.e. the Torah], *the Prophets and the Psalms* – **Luke 24: 44**

In other words, believing in the Resurrection isn't just factually accepting that a dead person is once again alive. It's a complete interpretation of life and death based on a correct understanding of the Bible. **John's Gospel** makes a similar point when the Risen Jesus says to the Disciples:

> *Because you have seen me, you have believed; blessed are those who have not seen and yet have believed* – **John 20: 29**

The point seeing to be that encountering the Risen Jesus is only valuable insofar as it leads to believing in the Word of God revealed in the Scriptures; other Christians can believe in the Word of God without meeting the Risen Jesus and that is, if anything, better still.

TOPIC 6.1 SCIENTIFIC & HISTORICAL-CRITICAL CHALLENGES TO THE RESURRECTION

The first systematic challenge to the Resurrection came from pagan philosophers in the Roman Empire, criticising the rose of Christianity. Much later, these challenges were re-stated by the philosophers of the Enlightenment.

Celsus vs Origen

Although the Edexcel Specification invites candidates to consider challenges to the Resurrection made during and after the Enlightenment, most of these arguments were framed much earlier, back in 180 CE by a pagan philosopher named **Celsus** in a book called *The True Word* (*Alethes Logos*).

Celsus launches two attacks on Christianity: he writes one section from the perspective of a Jew, interpreting Christianity as a corruption of Judaism and a misunderstanding of the Jewish Scriptures; in the second part, Celsus challenges Christianity head on by ridiculing the Resurrection of Jesus.

For half a century, Celsus went unanswered until the brilliant Christian scholar **Origen** (184-253 CE) took on the task of replying.

> *Origen's 'Against Celsus' (248 CE) is not just masterful debating but also preserves Celsus' original text (which otherwise would be lost to history) because Origen reproduces it word-for-word in order to reply to it.*

Celsus suggests that Jesus' Resurrection appearances may have been hallucinations produced by *"wishful thinking"*.

Origen [*right*] replies that the appearances were in broad daylight to groups of people and that there is no evidence in the Gospels that the witnesses were *"mentally unbalanced nor delirious"*.

Celsus suggests that Jesus' Resurrection was just a poor copy of the *fantastic tales* (*terateias*) of pagan heroes descending into the Underworld and returning (an argument used in the 20th century by **Sir James Frazer** and the **sociological approach** to interpreting Scripture; *c.f.* **Topic 4**).

Origen replies that, unlike the myths of gods like Osiris, Jesus dies publicly in a known place under a known Roman official. It is history, not mythology.

Celsus suggests that the Resurrection is a hoax and that the Disciples lied about meeting the Risen Jesus.

Origen argues that the *"the clear and certain proof"* for the Resurrection is the CHANGED LIVES of the disciples, going from frightened fugitives to brave martyrs who gained a *"power of endurance and resolution continued even to death"*. Why would anyone **invent** the story that Jesus had risen from the dead and then be willing to die for it themselves? A later Christian writer, Eusebius (311 CE), puts it like this:

> *Why would they die for him when he was dead, after they had deserted him when he was alive?* – **Eusebius**

This view was restated in by **Jacques Abbadie** (1698):

> *no one dies for a fiction which they have invented* – **Jacques Abbadie**

Origen's replies to Celsus were considered to be the last word on the subject for several centuries, but versions of Celsus' arguments returned, strengthened with scientific evidence, during the Enlightenment.

> *In drawing attention to the discrepancies in the resurrection narratives, Celsus has grasped the end of a thread that would eventually threaten to unravel the whole fabric of the accounts* – **William Lane Craig**

The Challenge of the Enlightenment

You have already looked at Enlightenment challenges to Scripture as part of **Topic 4 (Ways of Interpreting the Scripture)** *but I'll summarise those ideas here very briefly.*

The **Enlightenment** is often referred to as the "Age of Reason". This period begins with the ideas of Descartes in the 17th century and ends with the American and French Revolutions in the 18th century. Thinkers in France, Germany and Britain (especially Scotland) rejected many of the beliefs and traditions of previous generations and developed new ways of looking at the world based upon:

- **Rationalism:** truth comes from the use of reason, rather than accepting tradition or the authority of others
- **Empiricism:** all knowledge comes from our experience of the world using the 5 senses and is explored using scientific methods
- **Scepticism:** the reasonable starting position is to doubt the truth of all knowledge claims

These three factors combine together in the SCIENTIFIC WORLDVIEW that emerged during the Enlightenment and it was this worldview, rather than any particular scientific discovery, that undermined the plausibility of the Resurrection for many people.

> *The success of science encouraged people to believe that the world was governed by rational universal laws, discoverable by the human mind. Whether or not God was the author of such laws became increasingly irrelevant* – **Murray Rae**

Enlightenment scholars like **Thomas Hobbes** (1651) and **Jean Astruc** (1753) questioned the age and the authorship of the Old Testament.

Baron D'Holbach (1761) uses contradictions between the four Gospels to question whether they really could be **inspired** by God.

Hermann Reimarus (1774) went even further, arguing that the historical Jesus was a Jewish prophet-turned-political-revolutionary who never claimed to be the **Son of God** and whose disciples stole his body to fake the Resurrection.

Challenges like those of Reimarus were essentially the same arguments as the ones posed by Celsus centuries earlier, but this time they were strengthened by:

1. a new **scientific world-view** that was deeply sceptical about miracles
2. a **scientific approach to analyzing the Bible** which weakened confidence that the Gospels really were eyewitness accounts of the events they describe

Because of this, these challenges could not be countered with Origen's arguments quite so easily.

For example, **Thomas Woolston**'s *Six Discourses on the Miracles of Our Saviour* (1730) calls the Resurrection *"a monstrous fraud"*. Woolston proposes that the disciples stole Jesus' body, perhaps by bribing the guards or getting them drunk. Woolston echoes **David Hume**'s argument that, even if this is unlikely, it's a better explanation than the impossible idea of a resurrection:

> *Because the resurrection violates the course of Nature, no human testimony could possibly establish it, since it has the whole witness of Nature against it –* **Thomas Woolston**

In answer to Origen's view that the Disciples' willingness to die for the Resurrection was evidence they had not faked it, Woolston replies: *"Many other criminals and cheats have gone to their death proclaiming their innocence."*

> *What do you think? Is a willingness to die for your beliefs proof of your sincerity? Or will liars and fantasists stick to their crazy stories right to the end rather than admit the truth?*

The Resurrection as a Miracle

If naturalistic solutions (like a hoax or the Swoon Hypothesis – see p19) are rejected, then the Resurrection must be accepted as a miracle. This type of inductive logic is famously summarised by **Arthur Conan Doyle**'s fictional character Sherlock Holmes in the context of solving crimes:

> *when you have eliminated the impossible, whatever remains, however improbable, must be the truth* – **Arthur Conan Doyle**

This quote is widely misused. Sherlock Holmes was a (fictional) superhuman genius who could consider and eliminate all the possible alternatives, whereas ordinary humans (and Bible scholars) cannot consider every possible alternative. Nevertheless, the quote illustrates an important point that many of the naturalistic explanations of the Resurrection are deeply improbable whether or not God exists, whereas, *if* God exists and *if* God performs miracles, the Resurrection might not be that improbable at all.

> *That Jesus rose naturally from the dead is fantastically improbable. But I see no reason whatsoever to think that it is improbable that God raised Jesus from the dead* – **William Lane Craig**

But does God perform miracles? The Enlightenment brought about increasing scepticism regarding miracles and an interventionist God who would perform them.

- Enlightenment scientists building on **Isaac Newton's laws of motion** constructed a view of the universe operating according to unvarying laws. This world-view made the idea of those laws being suspended or broken seem less likely
- **Enlightenment Deism** proposed a God who created the universe but does not intervene in it

Part of the Deist argument was that miracles are simply impossible: the God of Deism does not perform miracles because that would be to go against the very laws that he himself has created. **Hermann Reimarus** (1754) summed up the Deist objection to miracles like this:

> *miracles contradict the order of creation and that therefore it is impossible for a rational man to believe in them* – **Hermann Reimarus**

Reimarus' view assumes that the *order of creation* does not allow for miracles. However, if the interventionist God of the Bible is real, then the *order of creation* is **supposed** to be contradicted on occasions – and the Resurrection would be one of those occasions.

David Hume *Of Miracles*

David Hume (1748) wrote an influential attack on miracles. However, Hume is clearly targeting the Resurrection in particular. He writes that we don't regard unusual events as a miracle because, despite being unusual, unusual events are **sometimes** observed to happen, but:

> *it is a miracle, that a dead man should come to life; because that has never been observed in any age or country* – **David Hume**

Hume argues that a miracle (of any sort) is, by definition, **the most improbable thing** that can happen. Therefore, if a miracle is reported, it is **always** more probable that the witness is lying or mistaken:

> *When anyone tells me, that he saw a dead man restored to life, I immediately consider with myself, whether it be more probable, that this person should either deceive or be deceived* – **David Hume**

Hume is not arguing that miracles CANNOT happen; he's arguing that a rational person should always prefer a naturalistic explanation of an apparent miracle, even if it's very unlikely, to the miracle itself, which is by definition **even more** unlikely.

Hume's argument has been criticised for being a CIRCULAR ARGUMENT. He starts with the assumption that the laws of nature are supported by exceptionless testimony, but this testimony is only exceptionless if we discount all reports of miracles. For example, Hume says that a dead man coming to life *"has never been observed in any age or country"* but the Resurrection **is** exactly such an observation.

Hume goes on to make a series of criticisms of testimonies about miracles that are clearly aimed at the Resurrection in particular:

- People enjoy incredible stories, which excite *"surprise and wonder"*
- Miracle stories tend to come from *"ignorant and barbarous nations"*
- These stories belong in the past, because over time societies progress out of believing in supernatural events

There's a very clear Enlightenment outlook here: scientific progress is curing European societies of belief in the supernatural, but religions are rooted in the pre-scientific past when people were more gullible.

Hume probably exaggerates how gullible people in the past really were. We have seen that disbelief and proposing naturalistic alternatives were the first responses to the accounts of the Resurrection, even in 1st century Palestine. This leads **N.T. Wright** (2003) to point out:

> *The discovery that dead people stay dead was not first made by the philosophers of the Enlightenment* – **N.T. Wright**

In other words, people in the 1st century knew perfectly well that dead men don't come back to life. It was just as improbable to them as it was to Hume 1700 years later.

Hume tackles the question of why a Disciple might invent a fiction that he was prepared to die for by suggesting that:

> *he may know his narrative to be false, and yet persevere with it, with the best intentions in the world, for the sake of promoting so holy a cause* – **David Hume**

Hume means that religious fanatics are prepared to die for a *holy cause* and they are also prepared to lie for that cause as well. If the Disciples were determined to spread Jesus' message of love and forgiveness of sins, they might have been prepared to invent the Resurrection to help spread the message.

Hume is certainly right that fanatics can tell lies for their cause with a clean conscience. This invites two responses:

1. Were the Disciples **really** fanatics of that sort? The New Testament presents them as rather simple men without great conviction: they run away when Jesus is arrested and Peter, the bravest, denies Jesus three times; they disbelieve in the Resurrection at first and they don't go to much effort to make their accounts of the Resurrection agree

2. Would the story of the Resurrection have made their *holy cause* more persuasive? In the Bible, most people disbelieve in the Resurrection when they first hear about it. Jesus' message of love and forgiveness could have been taught very effectively without the story of the Resurrection, so why invent an implausible story to support a moral teaching that is already appealing to most people?

Did the Enlightenment successfully challenge the Resurrection as a miracle?

YES

The Enlightenment saw the birth of science which shows us how the universe works according to fixed laws that do not require God to explain them. The Resurrection goes against our understanding of how the universe works.

Hume demonstrated that a miracle is so improbable that it's always reasonable to assume the witness is mistaken or lying. Jesus' Disciples came from an *"ignorant and barbarous"* time and were motivated to invent the Resurrection to promote their *"holy cause"*.

NO

The scientific laws describe how the universe is supposed to work on average, but if God exists then he is the source of those laws and can suspend or reverse them if he chooses. Science doesn't show that a miracle is impossible or even unlikely.

Hume's argument is circular, because he assumes that dead men never come back to life then uses this to argue that one should never believe a report of a dead man coming back to life. Hume's cynical view of people in the past as gullible or fanatical does not match the descriptions in the Gospels.

The Resurrection as a Fictional Event

In place of miracles, scholars of the Enlightenment offered NATURALISTIC explanations of the Resurrection. One of these is the "Theft Hypothesis" that Jesus' Disciples stole his corpse to fake the Resurrection (perhaps not intentionally: they might merely have moved the body then the women arrived and, finding the empty tomb, leapt to conclusions that Jesus had risen from the dead).

The Theft Hypothesis seems to be as old as Christianity itself, since **Matthew 28: 11-15** references it being spread around by the Jewish leaders and **Celsus** brings it up as well. The standard objection was given by **Origen**, that the Disciples would not embrace suffering, persecution and death for the sake of a lie.

A different argument that the Resurrection is fictional is the "Swoon Hypothesis", which argues that Jesus did not really die on the cross but that his Disciples misinterpreted his reappearance as a miraculous resurrection.

The Swoon Hypothesis

This is the suggestion that Jesus passed out ('swooned') on the cross but did not die. He later recovered consciousness in the tomb.

The main support for this argument is medical. Jesus died after 6 hours on the cross, which is a very short time. **Mark 15: 44** records Pontius Pilate being surprised to learn that Jesus had died so soon. **Justus Lipsius** (1629) argues that healthy adults would suffer crucifixion for 2-4 days, up to 9 days in some cases. This lends support to the idea that Jesus might have 'swooned'.

Karl Friedrich Bahrdt (1741-1792) proposes a conspiracy theory, that Jesus' followers gave him a drug that brought on a near-death state so that he would *appear* to die on the cross then later recover in safety. Bahrdt thought that Jesus pretended to be a spiritual Messiah to encourage the Jews to abandon their belief in a violent Kingly Messiah. The creation of a completely separate religion ('Christianity') was not part of the plan.

Scholars like Bahrdt argue that Jesus was a member of a secret society and that the man or men in white robes described in the Synoptic Gospels (e.g. **Mark 16: 5**) were conspirators who had opened the tomb and helped Jesus revive. The women arrived at the tomb and surprised them in the act, but mistook them for angels. Since the **Essenes** wore white robes, this theory often proposes that Jesus was an Essene and that the Essenes revived him and helped him recover at one of their desert monasteries.

Not all supporters of the Swoon Hypothesis agree with this conspiracy theory. **Heinrich Paulus** (1761-1851) supposes that Jesus went into a coma on the cross but awoke naturally because of the cold air of the tomb.

Critics of the Swoon Hypothesis point out that Jesus had been beaten several times and flogged by the Roman soldiers before the Crucifixion. He was too weak to carry his own cross so **Simon of Cyrene** was made to carry it for him. Given his physical state, it's quite possible he would have died quickly.

Moreover, Roman soldiers who had carried out hundreds of crucifixions would not have allowed prisoners to be taken down if there was any reason to suppose they were still alive.

> These executioners knew what they were doing, and theories that Jesus somehow physically survived the cross represent a combination of fantasy, revisionism, and half-baked science – **Bruce Chilton**

More important, the wounds resulting from crucifixion would have been traumatic. **Flavius Josephus** (99 CE) describes friends who were crucified but rescued and says two of the three died from their injuries despite the best medical care on offer. **David Strauss** (1865) argues that it's impossible to believe that *"a being who had stolen half dead out of the sepulcher* [i.e. tomb]*"* could have convinced the Disciples that he had returned to full and supernatural life.

> The suggestion that a man so critically wounded then went on to appear to the disciples on various occasions in Jerusalem and Galilee is pure fantasy – **William Lane Craig**

> The Swoon Hypothesis is popular with some Muslims because the Qur'an states that Jesus did not die on the cross. Some believe that a substitute replaced the real Jesus.

Is the Resurrection a fictional event?

YES

Naturalistic solutions should always be preferred to supernatural ones. This is the 'Principle of Parsimony' (also known as OCCAM'S RAZOR). We know that hoaxes occur and that people who seem to be dead sometimes recover. It makes more sense to suppose that something like this explains the apparent 'Resurrection'.

A conspiracy theory would explain the disciples' beliefs and Jesus' escape from the tomb. If an Essene sect drugged Jesus then later revived him it would explain his suspiciously quick 'death' on the cross and the appearance of the white-robed men at the empty tomb. The disciples mistook them for angels because they weren't "in on it". The conspiracy hoped to change Jewish beliefs, but did not intend to start a new religion.

NO

These naturalistic solutions are not 'parsimonious' at all: they just involve more speculation. Why would the first Christian disciples be prepared to suffer and die for what they knew to be a hoax? How could the crucified Jesus recover from his wounds enough to get out of a tomb with a stone rolled across the exit?

Enlightenment scholars did love their conspiracy theories and other people still do, but these theories involve large groups of people working in absolute secrecy and no one telling what they know. How could Jesus have been part of an Essence secret plot that his closest disciples knew nothing about? How could the Essenes have healed him of his wounds enough to pose as the Resurrected Son of God in front of people who knew him?

The Resurrection as a Myth

In the 19th century, the view of the **Resurrection as a fiction** lost popularity, but sceptics continued to propose naturalistic alternatives. One is the idea that the resurrection is a **myth** and that 1st century beliefs about pagan gods and Jewish prophets got 'attached' to the story of Jesus.

This is another view that was first proposed by **Celsus** in the 2nd century. Celsus noticed the similarity between Jesus' death and resurrection with the character of certain pagan gods.

The Egyptian god **Osiris** is a good example. Osiris' birth was heralded by a star in the heavens. Osiris was a healer and a prophet but he was betrayed by someone close to him and murdered; his body was hidden away — though not for long, as he returned in a miraculous resurrection to reign in heaven as the god who judges the dead and assigns rewards in paradise or punishments in hell

Anthropologists (who study ancient cultures) describe this sort of being as a DYING-AND-RISING GOD. There are a lot of them in different mythologies all around the world. Although Jesus is the best-known example of a resurrected figure, he is far from the only one.

The Ancient Jews did not have myths about a dying-and-rising god, but they had myths about comparable figures. In **Unit 1 (Context of the New Testament)**, you studied the **Suffering Servant** in **Isaiah** who is supposed to suffer and die and then be restored to life by God. The prophet **Elijah** did not die a mortal death but was taken up into heaven in a fiery chariot; it was widely believed by 1st century Jews that Elijah was immortal and would return to Earth one day.

According to the "Mythicist Theory", after Jesus' death, pagan myths (such as **Osiris**) and Jewish myths (such as the **Suffering Servant** and **Elijah**) became mixed up with Jesus' story, including the all-important dying-and-rising motif. This happened gradually over many re-tellings (rather like 'Chinese Whispers' where the original message gets changed out of all recognition).

A crucial part of this argument is that the Disciples originally believed in a SPIRITUAL RESURRECTION – that Jesus had risen as a spirit – but that over time the myth took over that Jesus had returned to physical life. There are details that support this view:

- The earliest Christian writer is **Paul** and his encounter with the Risen Jesus is more like a spiritual vision. Paul never mentions the empty tomb or the physical appearances of Jesus.
- **Mark's Gospel** (which originally seems to lack Resurrection scenes) was written perhaps 10-20 years after Paul's letters and the other Gospels (which *do* feature Resurrection scenes) perhaps 10-20 years after Mark.

Even in the later Gospels, there are tensions between the scenes that show a belief in a physical Resurrection (e.g. touching Jesus' hands and feet) and more mystical encounters (e.g. the **road to Emmaus**). This makes sense if the physical Resurrection scenes have been added in later but the mystical scenes are older and more authentic.

Jewish followers added to this vision all sorts of details from **Isaiah's Servant Songs** and legends about **Elijah**. When Gentiles joined the Church they added details from their pagan culture, such as a dying-and-rising god like **Osiris** who physically comes back to life.

David Strauss, *The Life of Jesus Critically Examined*

David Strauss (1835), one of the most influential Bible scholars of the century, refuted the "Theft" and "Swoon" Hypotheses and proposed the view that the Resurrection was really a **myth**. Strauss' wrote *Das Leben Jesu* when only 27 and argued that the disciples attributed to Jesus all the miracles that Jewish myths had said that a Messiah would do. By 'myths', Strauss means:

> *the expression of primitive Christian ideas formulated in unintentionally poeticizing sagas and looking very like history* – **David Strauss**

In other words, a myth is UNINTENTIONAL POETRY that looks like HISTORY. Strauss admits there is spiritual truth in these myths – in that sense, they are not *false* – but they are not *history* either. Strauss thinks of a myth as a sort of dream that humans naturally come up with to express feelings that are important to them.

Strauss' book caused an uproar across Europe. The **Earl of Shaftesbury** called it "*the most pestilential book ever vomited out of the jaws of hell!*" Strauss lost his job at the University of Zürich due to the controversy and never worked as a teacher again.

There are problems with Strauss' theory. As you noted when studying **Topic 1.1 (Prophecy Concerning the Messiah)**, there are many ways in which Jesus does *not* fit the template for the Jewish **Messiah**, the **Suffering Servant** or the **son of David**. If a mythic detail like the Resurrection was added to Jesus' story by later Christians, why were awkward details like his being from Galilee rather than Judea not removed while they were at it?

The Gospels do not read like pagan myths or psychological wishes. They contain very specific times (e.g. 23 April, 33 CE for the Resurrection) and places (Jerusalem) and psychological motives (blasphemy, political expediency). **Julius Müller** (1844) argues that *real* myths take place in "*the mysterious gloom of grey antiquity*" but the Gospels are not set in 'ancient times' but in recent memory of the first believers.

> *One cannot imagine how such a series of legends could arise ... if eyewitnesses were still at hand who could be questioned respecting the truth*– **Julius Müller**

Many scholars argue that the 30 years between the Crucifixion and the appearance of the first Christian writings is not long enough for the process of myth-making to take place.

Nonetheless, Strauss' theory does show how a belief in the Resurrection could come about without the Disciples of Jesus behaving deceitfully or insincerely or even particularly gullibly, which makes his theory an improvement on the "Theft" and "Swoon" Hypotheses. He also introduced the idea of a 'myth' as a story which is not historically true but which is not a simple falsehood or fiction either – myths can express true ideas in story form.

> *The Mythicist Hypothesis is not to be confused with the 'Christ Myth Theory' that argues that the ENTIRETY of Jesus' life is a myth, not just the Resurrection. This isn't Strauss' position: he thinks the historical really Jesus existed. The Christ Myth Theory doesn't carry much weight among Bible scholars – but it's popular online (of course!) and you'll find a lot of websites dedicated to the idea that Jesus is a made-up person.*

Is the Resurrection a myth?

YES	NO
People in the 1st century viewed the world in a mythological way and expected their heroes to live mythic lives. By adding mythic details to Jesus' story, they wouldn't have thought they were deceiving anyone. Jewish-Christians would re-tell Jesus' story to make him more like Elijah (going up to heaven but then returning to Earth) and Gentiles would make him more like the dying-and-rising pagan gods.	Myths do not 'pop up' like mushrooms; they take lifetimes to develop and evolve. However, the first Christian writings appeared within a couple of decades of Jesus' life, death and resurrection and in a community where the original witnesses were still on hand to describe their experiences. This cannot be said of Elijah or Osiris who lived in *"the mysterious gloom of grey antiquity."*
The 1st century Christians lived in a world before the study of history had been discovered. It was natural for them to create *"unintentionally poetic sagas"* to communicate their intense love and reverence for Jesus: they exaggerated his achievements in the only way they knew how, by making him resemble the great figures of mythology, including coming back to life.	The Ancient Greeks and Romans had their historians too and they knew enough to be sceptical about myths and legends. The idea that Christians started with a belief in a purely spiritual Resurrection than mythologized it into a physical Resurrection fails to account for the historical details: the Empty Tomb, the testimony of the women, the meetings with the Risen Jesus who can be touched and eats.

The Resurrection as an Event in the Experience of the Disciples

As anthropology developed in the 20th century, the view of the **Resurrection as a myth** came to seem less plausible. A different naturalistic interpretation was that the Resurrection appearances were in fact hallucinations or visions. This idea was also put forward by **David Strauss** (1835) who argues the Disciples hallucinated Jesus' return from the dead because:

> *incapable of thinking of Jesus as dead, they were deluded into thinking that he had risen and appeared to them* – **David Strauss**

Celsus had suggested this back in the 2nd century and **Origen** rejected it on the grounds that the Disciples were *"neither mentally unbalanced nor delirious."* However, the development of Psychology shows that otherwise-healthy people under conditions of great emotional stress can show psychotic symptoms (such as hallucinations) while appearing normal in other respects.

Reports from Singapore General Hospital following the tsunami tragedy in Thailand (2004) describe accounts of "ghost sightings" among survivors who had lost loved ones. There may well be cultural or religious factors since many Thais believe that spirits may be put to rest only by relatives. Neurologist **Oliver Sacks** explains how such hallucinations can be psychologically comforting:

> *seeing the face or hearing the voice of one's deceased spouse, siblings, parents or child... may play an important part in the mourning process* – **Oliver Sacks**

Christian Weisse (1838) writes that the Resurrection *"has its source in the disciples' experience of the presence of Christ"* – but all the precise details were from their imaginations. **Ernest Renan** (1863) claims that the Resurrection was created by the imagination of **Mary Magdalene** and passed on to the Disciples as a sort of MASS HYSTERIA:

> *The little Christian society ... resuscitated Jesus in their hearts by the intense love which they bore toward him* – **Ernest Renan**

Jack Kent, *The Psychological Origins of the Resurrection Myth*

Jack Kent (1999) makes a contribution to the **'Habermas-Flew Debate'** between **Gary Habermas** (theist) and **Antony Flew** (sceptic) concerning the Resurrection. Kent offers a psychiatric interpretation of the 'Resurrection experiences' of the early disciples, based on current medical knowledge.

Kent argues that the women at the tomb and later the Disciples experienced *"normal, grief-related hallucinations."* **Peter** experienced additional guilt over denying Jesus before the Crucifixion; **Paul** experienced inner conflict over his part in the stoning to death of Stephen and his persecution of Christians.

Kent proposes these men suffered a *"conversion disorder,"* a recognized psychiatric illness that can occur in times of great anxiety and self-doubt. Paul's blindness after his vision of Jesus might have been PSYCHOSOMATIC (it existed only in his mind).

However, **Gary Habermas** points out that conversion disorder usually occurs in women (up to five times more often), adolescents and people with poor education or low socioeconomic status; it also occurs in former soldiers. None of this applies to Paul although the other Disciples seem to have been poor and uneducated. The women who visited the empty tomb were probably uneducated but they don't seem to have been poor (they helped fund Jesus' ministry and one is described as the wife of Herod's official).

The idea of 'holy hallucinations' avoids the idea of the Disciples or the later Christians fictionalising or carrying out a hoax: they are sincere witnesses, but mistaken.

However, there are three important questions unanswered:

- Why did the hallucinations stop? The Gospels report the Risen Jesus ascending into Heaven, which **Luke-Acts** claims took place 40 days after the Resurrection. Why didn't the mass hysteria continue to spread to other believers, just as the first hallucinations had?
- Why did the witnesses all experience the *same* hallucination? Hallucinations are SUBJECTIVE – they are unique to each person – yet the Disciples all seem to have shared the same hallucination. Even in the case of mass hysteria, individuals do not all experience the same thing
- Why was the tomb empty? Because the hallucination hypothesis does not explain the empty tomb, another naturalistic explanation is needed to cover this, such as 'Theft' or 'Swoon'.

The Objective Vision Hypothesis

Some Christian scholars argue that hallucinations might be genuine religious experiences. **Hans Grass** (1964) claims that Jesus' body remained dead and his Resurrection appearances were God-given **visions**; this is the "Objective Vision Hypothesis" in which the Resurrection appearances were genuine supernatural visions, but not physical encounters. **Theodor Keim** (1872) calls this sort of vision a *"telegram from heaven."*

The idea of 'objective visions' explains why a group of people could share the same hallucination. However, the problem is that such visions are DECEPTIVE. Why would God send a vision that fooled his followers into thinking a physical Resurrection had taken place? Moreover, why believe in a God who causes utterly realistic visions but not a God who can raise the dead to life?

William Lane Craig dismisses this sort of theory, arguing that:

> *[God] would have no conceivable reason for skipping the physical miracle of a resurrection and befuddling his earnest followers into the bargain* – **William Lane Craig**

This theory, just like the naturalistic Hallucination Theory, rejects the Gospel accounts of the Risen Jesus' bodily form (such as touching his hands and feet) as later inventions.

Is the Resurrection a hallucination or vision?

YES

We know that people suffering bereavement can hallucinate their loved one is still alive and this might explain **Mary Magdalene**. Conversion disorder' can produce hallucinations in people like **Paul** and **Peter** who were suffering great guilt and moral confusion. Belief in the Resurrection began as visions, only later being changed to physical encounters.

We know that mass hysteria can be contagious, especially in a tightly-knit group of people under great stress with powerful beliefs. When one person starts hallucinating, it spreads to the others. The hallucinations might even be genuine visions, sent by God, to inspire the Disciples' faith.

NO

Hallucinations are subjective, but those who met the Risen Jesus all experienced the same thing. **Paul** does not fit the profile for conversion disorder, being older and educated; we don't have enough information to know whether **Peter** and the other Disciples cud have suffered from this disorder but it doesn't fit with their words and behaviour in Luke-Acts.

Mass hysteria is still subjective and produces different hallucinations. Moreover, this doesn't explain why the hallucinations stopped after 40 days or why the tomb was empty. If God sent visions of Jesus, then the Disciples misunderstood those visions as a physical Resurrection, which brings into question God's wisdom and omnipotence.

Evaluating Challenges to the Resurrection

Naturalistic interpretations to the Resurrection are as old as accounts of the Resurrection itself. The Theft Hypothesis was proposed by Jewish critics of Christianity and **Celsus** (185 CE) proposed the Mythicist and Hallucination Hypotheses.

During and after the Enlightenment, the Theft Hypothesis was re-stated very forcefully. This was part of **rationalist interpretations** of Scripture (c.f. **Topic 4.1 Ways of Interpreting the Scriptures**). The rationalists were **Deists** who were prepared to accept the moral value of Jesus' teachings about compassion and repentance, but believed Christianity had been distorted by a belief in miracles and the supernatural. The Theft Hypothesis allows for Jesus to remain a wise and holy man who taught a simple lesson of goodness, but his fanatical disciples corrupted this by faking his Resurrection. By extension, the established churches which teach these miracles continue to betray Jesus' original moral message.

The Theft Hypothesis fell out of favour in the 19th century. Improvements in Bible criticism made it clear how sophisticated the early beliefs about the Resurrection were and how sincere the first Christians were in their faith. The related Swoon Hypothesis was demolished by **David Strauss** (1865) who argues that a survivor of crucifixion would have been too frail to have convinced the Disciples that he had been resurrected or produce such awe and worship in them.

The Mythicist Hypothesis became popular in the 19th and early 20th century. It is part of **sociological** and **literary interpretations** of Scripture and was given a huge boost by the popularity of **Sir James Frazer**'s *The Golden Bough* (1915) and the new field of anthropology, which studies ancient cultures and looks for common links across all religions. Anthropology tends to view religious beliefs as expressions of social situations, so this view regards the Resurrection as a way for early Christians to express their beliefs about Jesus in story form and make their new religion resemble their previous (pagan or Jewish) belief.

However, anthropology developed over the 20th century and the earlier views of Frazer and his admirers came to be seen as simplistic. Myths do not grow up like mushrooms in a short amount of time and the Gospels, when subjected to literary analysis, do not resemble myths.

The Mythicist Theory links to the views of **Rudolf Bultmann**, which you studied in **Topic 4 (Ways of Interpreting the Scriptures)**. Bultmann interprets the Gospel stories as myths that once made sense to pre-modern people but which cannot be accepted by scientific people today. He argues that the New Testament must be DE-MYTHOLOGIZED to understand the symbolic meaning of the Resurrection and make it relevant to today.

A slightly different view comes from **R. Alan Culpepper (Topic 5.2 Why Did Jesus Have to Die?)** who argues that we have to read the accounts of the Resurrection like a novel in order to *"read the gospel as the author's original audience read it"*. This is because, ever since the Enlightenment, modern readers automatically separate literal and symbolic meaning, but the 1st century readers of the Gospels did not make such a distinction.

In 1967, **Raymond E. Brown** pronounced naturalistic theories about the Resurrection as failures:

> *Serious scholars pay little attention to these fictional reconstructions* – **Raymond E. Brown**

However, the Hallucination Hypothesis is coming back into favour. This was first popularised by **David Strauss** as part of the **historical interpretation** of Scripture but it lapsed in the 20th century when Psychology took a more scientific, less speculative direction. According to **Gary Habermas**, the theory is growing in popularity again the 21st century.

The new popularity of the Hallucination Hypothesis is perhaps due to changes in the psychology of mental disorders, which increasingly focuses on the minor abnormal disorders that affect otherwise-normal people.

This makes it more plausible when psychologists like **Jack Kent** propose that the Disciples could hallucinate for a temporary period then fully recover, perhaps as a response to stress in their lives. However, not everyone is happy with loose and easily-applied diagnoses like *"conversion disorder"*. **Allen Frances** (2012) complains that the new medical textbook for mental disorders (**DSM-5**) *"medicalizes"* healthy experiences like grief, anger or forgetfulness, turning them into mental disorders. Writers like Jack Kent are 'medicalizing' the Resurrection in the same way.

Has the Resurrection been successfully disproved?

YES	NO
Naturalistic explanations of the Empty Tomb and the appearances of the Risen Jesus will always be more persuasive to scientifically-minded people than the idea of someone miraculously rising from the dead. In particular, we now understand false beliefs better than ever and can diagnose why the Disciples might have become convinced that their Lord had returned from the dead.	It's important to remember that Jesus didn't raise **himself** from the dead (which would be very improbable) – he was raised from the dead BY GOD. This is a very different proposition. If God exists and can perform miracles, then the idea that the Disciples suffered from strange, intense but temporary delusions doesn't look nearly as plausible as an explanation of the Resurrection.
Even though there are problems with individual naturalistic explanations, it remains the case that it is more likely that ONE of them is in fact the truth than that the laws of nature were violated by ringing a man back to life.	1st century Christians weren't gullible fools. It was clearly as difficult for them to accept the Resurrection as it is for so-called scientifically-minded modern people. They accepted the Resurrection as a fact because the weight of evidence pointed towards it.

Frank Morison, *Between Sunset and Dawn*

The Edexcel Anthology includes this passage as extract #8. Rather confusingly, it dates the extract from 2015. Take note: the passage is from Frank Morison's book Who Moved The Stone?' *which was **originally** published in 1930!*

Frank Morison (real name: **Albert Henry Ross**, 1881-1950) is a journalist who wrote this classic piece of Christian APOLOGETICS (defence) nearly 100 years ago. Morison grew up agreeing with the then-new challenges to Christianity from *"the German critics"* (people like **David Strauss**) and decided to research a book exposing the Christian religion as a 'myth'.

However, while researching the book, Morison came to the opposite conclusion, that the evidence pointed towards the Resurrection being a historical fact.

it effected a revolution in my thought. Things emerged from old-world story that previously I should have thought impossible – **Frank Morison**

Who Moved the Stone? goes through the final 24 hours of Jesus' life and the days that follow in the style of a lawyer sifting evidence, calling witnesses and discrediting them and arriving at a conclusion which is 'beyond all reasonable doubt'. It reads like a detective story, rather like *Sherlock Holmes*, with the sense of a mystery being unravelled through painstaking logic. It was a best-seller in its day and has been reprinted ten times since.

If you like Edwardian 'whodunnit?' detective stories like Agatha Christie then you should definitely read this slim book. You can read the full text on websites (e.g. ***www.gospeltruth.net****) or buy a Kindle or second-hand print edition for under £3.*

Between Sunset & Dawn is the 8th chapter of Morison's book. Earlier in the book, Morison discusses the tangled motives for the chief priests in arresting Jesus on the Passover night (he agrees with the Synoptic Gospels' dating of this) and explores how Jesus' Disciples were split into two groups: **Peter** and **John** (Morison identifies the 'Beloved Disciple' as John son of Zebedee and follows John's Gospel's account here) follow the guards to the city and are left inside the city walls during the Sabbath; the other Disciples run away and Morison concludes they would have escaped to the village of Bethany nearby to warn the sisters Mary and Martha of what had happened.

Morison goes on to analyse the **trial before Pilate** in detail, exploring **Pontius Pilate**'s psychology as well as the complicated legal processes at work. Morison's technique is to focus on the things that are left unsaid and the details that are left unexplained.

For example, Morison argues that Pilate was under emotional pressure from his wife to free Jesus, based on **Matthew 27: 19** which reports that Claudia had a dream about Jesus and begged her husband: *"Don't have anything to do with that innocent man!"*

Morison produces a HARMONISATION of the four Gospels, blending their accounts together to produce a single, plausible narrative. He uses elements from the **rationalist approach** (he ignores miraculous elements, such as the healing of Malchus' ear in **Luke 22: 51**) and the **historical approach** to interpreting Scripture (he applies knowledge of Jewish and Roman legal processes and the archaeological layout of Jerusalem to reconstruct events like a historian).

In chapter 8, Morison considers what happened to Jesus' body on Easter morning. Right at the outset, he dismisses the idea proposed by **Celsus** and later by **Herman Reimarus** that the Disciples stole Jesus' body from the tomb.

> no great moral structure like the Early Church, based as it was upon lifelong persecution and personal suffering, could have reared its head upon a statement which every one of the eleven apostles knew to be a lie.

Morison is repeating the objections made by **Origen** and later **Jacques Abbadie** (1698) that "*no one dies for a fiction which they have invented.*" **Thomas Woolston** (1730) disagrees, pointing out "*criminals and cheats have gone to their death proclaiming their innocence.*" There is also the possibility of a conspiracy that the Disciples might not have known about, such as a rival group of disciples (Woolston suggests the mysterious **Essenes**). However, most scholars agree with Morison's verdict on this.

Morison goes on to consider 6 possible explanations for the women discovering an empty tomb:

1. Joseph of Arimathea removed Jesus' body
2. The Roman authorities removed Jesus' body
3. The Jewish authorities removed Jesus' body
4. Jesus was not really dead and later recovered in the tomb
5. The women went to the wrong tomb
6. No one visited the tomb and the story is a myth

Joseph of Arimathea removed Jesus' body

All the Gospels agree that a Jewish leader named **Joseph of Arimathea** provided an unused tomb for Jesus' body. It is plausible that this was only a temporary arrangement and that Joseph then moved the body to a more permanent resting place.

Morison points out an initial problem with this explanation: why would Joseph remove the body in the middle of the night? This would be difficult and inconvenient and there was no need to hide what he was doing. Even if he arrived with workmen first thing on the morning after the Sabbath, the women would have encountered him there, rather than an empty tomb.

However, Morison admits that Joseph might have had *some* reason to want to avoid attention so it's possible he removed the body in the night. This would explain **Mary Magdalene**'s message that "*they have taken away the Lord and we do not know where they have laid him!*"

Morison considers Joseph's possible motives:

1. He was a pious Jew and did not want a body to remain hanging overnight (forbidden by **Deuteronomy 21: 23**)
2. He was a secret follower of Jesus and wanted to show his teacher a last respect

Morison rejects the first theory because no effort was made to bury the two thieves who all four Gospels describe as being crucified alongside Jesus.

However, if Joseph was a secret follower of Jesus, then he would have been pleased for Jesus' body to remain in his tomb: it would have been an honour – or, as Morison sums up the view that Joseph moved the body: *"overwhelmingly, psychology is against it."*

If Joseph moved the body to a better location, then *that* location would have become a *"tomb or shrine becoming the centre of veneration or worship."*

However, there were never any rumours of alternative resting places for Jesus' body.

> Strange though it may appear, the only way in which we can account for the absence of this phenomenon is the explanation offered in the Gospels, viz. that the tomb was known, was investigated a few hours after the burial, and that the body had disappeared.

Morison concludes that, although the empty tomb is unlikely, the idea of Joseph of Arimathea removing the body but concealing its new location is even more unlikely.

Evaluating Morison on the burial

Morison assumes that the story of Joseph of Arimathea providing a tomb for Jesus is historical in the first place but some critics suggest otherwise. **Bart Ehrman** argues that standard practice for the Romans was to bury crucified convicts together in an unmarked shallow grave where they would probably be dug up and eaten by animals – the ultimate disgrace. **John Dominic Crossan** (1994) proposes that Jesus' body was *"eaten by scavenging dogs."* This is known as the 'Shallow Grave' Theory.

In support of this, it is very improbable that Pilate would have made an exception to Roman practice for Jesus. Joseph of Arimathea is a character never previously mentioned in the Gospels and never mentioned again; 'Arimathea' is an unknown place and may well be fictional.

The earliest reference to Jesus' death and resurrection is from **Paul**, who only states that Jesus was *buried* (**1 Corinthians 15: 4**) but never mentions a tomb. The tomb could have been a fiction composed by **Mark's Gospel** which was then copied by the other Gospels.

The authorities (Jewish or Roman) removed Jesus' body

Morison lumps his 2nd and 3rd explanations together, because the same objections apply to both of them.

Morison thinks it is unlikely that *"a very obstinate man"* such as Pilate would have changed his mind about Jesus' burial once his decision was made. He points out that the records show the priests requesting, not the removal of Jesus' body, but a guard of soldiers to prevent *anyone else* removing the body. However, Morison has a more powerful objection to this idea:

> For if the Priests induced Pilate to change the burial place, or to authorize their doing so, they must have known the ultimate and final resting-place, and in that event they would never have been content with the obviously unsatisfactory and untrue statement that the disciples had stolen the body.

The rumour that the Disciples stole the body of Jesus is mentioned in **Matthew 28: 13** and is repeated by **Celsus** in the 2nd century CE. But if the authorities knew where the body was, there would be no need for such a rumour: they could have announced the true burial place and *"destroyed forever the credibility of anyone asserting the physical resurrection of Jesus."*

> It is the complete failure of anyone to produce the remains, or to point to any tomb, official or otherwise, in which they were said to lie, which ultimately destroys every theory based upon the human removal of the body.

Morison's point is a strong one because we know that the Jewish authorities and later the Roman authorities persecuted Christians for their beliefs, but did not think to disprove them by showing that *they* had removed the body.

Evaluating Morison on the body

Even if the authorities did remove Jesus' body, producing it again to silence Christian claims of the Resurrection would not have been easy. **Luke-Acts** states that the Disciples did not start preaching the Resurrection until after the **Ascension**, which took place 40 days later. This means the body of Jesus would have been at least 7 weeks old – probably no longer recognizable enough to put a stop to the Christian claims.

Furthermore, in order to make this counter-claim, the authorities would have to admit what they had done. For the Jewish authorities, this would be admitting to desecrating a grave, which is very sinful in Judaism. For the Romans, it would have been a huge deviation from their normal procedure for crucifying criminals where the body was left to hang in a public place so that everyone can see the corpse deteriorate – and also graverobbing, which would possibly start a riot (the very thing Pilate wanted to prevent, according to the **political expediency** argument about **Why Jesus Had to Die**, *c.f.* **Topic 5**).

Jesus did not really die on the cross

This is the 'Swoon Theory' (p19) proposed by **Karl Bahrdt** and **Heinrich Paulus** during the Enlightenment. It also includes the popular Muslim view that Jesus was rescued from the cross or else someone else died in his place.

Morison mentions **Karl Venturini**'s 1800 version of the Swoon Theory: Jesus survived the crucifixion and was rescued by his **Essene** allies, made surreptitious appearances to his followers but finally died a natural death 40 days later, which his Disciples mistook for him 'ascending into heaven'.

Morison sums up the implausibility of this from a medical standpoint:

> It ignores the deadly character of the wounds inflicted upon Jesus, the frightful laceration of the hands and feet, the loss of strength through the ebbing away of blood, the hopelessness of human aid during the critical moments when it would be most needed, the tight-drawn bandages of the grave, the heavy stone.

(Although to be fair, many versions of the Swoon Theory are also conspiracy theories and propose Jesus had help moving the stone and taking off his bandages.)

Morison's refers to the *"death blow to this theory"* from **David Strauss** (1865). Strauss points out that, even if he did survive crucifixion and escape the *sepulchre* (tomb), Jesus would have been

> *a being who had stolen half dead out of the sepulchre, who crept about weak and ill and wanting medical treatment* – **David Strauss**

Somebody in this condition could not have

> *given the disciples the impression that he was a Conqueror over death and the grave, the Prince of Life* – **David Strauss**

Evaluating Morison on the 'swoon'

There are not many defenders today of the Swoon Theory (also known as the Apparent Death Theory or ADT). Morison's (and Strauss') arguments don't have many critics:

> *Anyone who imagines that the survivor of a crucifixion would be in a state to convince anyone that he was the victorious conqueror of death clearly has very little idea what a crucifixion was like. To put the matter mildly, people did not walk away from it* – **Christopher Bryan**

Nonetheless, the best-selling book *Holy Blood, Holy Grail* (1982) speculates that **Pontius Pilate** was bribed to allow Jesus to be rescued before he was dead. The book proposes Jesus went to live in the south of France with his wife, **Mary Magdalene**, and his descendants still exist today.

> *Sounds familiar? Dan Brown lifted the theory for his 2003 hit novel (and 2006 film with Tom Hanks) 'The Da Vinci Code'. It's a fun story but it's only plausible if you're the sort of person who loves conspiracy theories ...*

The Women Made a Mistake

Morison credits this theory to **Prof. Kirsopp Lake** (Lake's book *The Resurrection of Jesus Christ* was published in 1907). Lake argues that, in the darkness before dawn, the women arrived at the wrong tomb (he claims: *"the neighborhood of Jerusalem is full of rock tombs"*) which would be a naturalistic explanation for the account of the tomb (i) being open and (ii) having no body inside.

Mark 16: 5 describes the women finding *"a young man dressed in a white robe"* sitting inside the tomb. The other Gospels represent this person as an angel, but Lake thinks (and Morison agrees) that this was a human being. Lake argues that this was a gardener who tried to tell the women they had come to the wrong place: *"See the place where they laid him"* (**Mark 16: 6**) is the gardener trying to indicate *a different tomb*.

Lake proposes that the women were already running in fear and only half-heard the gardener's instruction and misunderstood the words to refer to the empty ledge in the tomb where a body would be laid.

The obvious criticism of this view is that, as soon as they were notified, the Disciples came to the tomb and checked for themselves (as described by **Luke** and **John's Gospel**): did they also go to the wrong tomb, in broad daylight?

Lake's response is that the other Disciples had *already left* Jerusalem: they had returned home to Galilee. Lake thinks that the Disciples had visions or hallucinations of the Risen Jesus in Galilee *before* they knew anything about the empty tomb. When they returned to Jerusalem, they met the women who told them about Jesus' body 'disappearing'.

Morison makes several criticisms of this theory:

1. The Gospels do not present *all* the Disciples as running away. **Peter** remained in Jerusalem; so perhaps did the 'Beloved Disciple' (who may be **John**). Earlier in his book, Morison argues that the other Disciples only escaped as far as nearby Bethany, not all the way to Galilee.
2. It would be very strange for the Disciples to abandon these women in Jerusalem for weeks, especially since some were their own family and mothers. Morison argues that if a group of women felt safe to visit Jesus' tomb, a group of men would surely have felt safe to stay in hiding in Jerusalem.
3. Why would the gardener have been sitting *inside* an empty tomb?

The final criticism links back to the arguments about someone removing the body:

> Here was the one man who could have spoken with complete and final authority; whose slightest word could have blown the whole flimsy story to the winds.

4. If the Jewish authorities wanted to disprove the Christian claims about the Resurrection, , they could bring in the gardener as a witness to the women's mistake, yet there is no reference to this even as a rumour

Evaluating Morison on the location of the tomb

As you will see when you study **Ian Wilson**'s anthology extract #9 (p38), there are several contenders for the true tomb of Jesus, so it's certainly possible for the women to have gone to the wrong tomb. Nevertheless, **Paul Gwynne** (2000) agrees with Morison: *"the 'mistaken tomb' theory has very few serious supporters these days."*

> *it is difficult to imagine how [a wrong tomb] mistake would not have been quickly corrected* – **C.E.B. Cranfield**

Nevertheless, Morison does agree with Lake on several key points that he develops later in his book:

- Morison agrees with Lake that the women were frightened away by a strange man in the tomb and he shares Lake's view that the other Gospels are fictionalizing when they represent this person as an angel
- Morison also thinks it likely that the women did not understand what the man was trying to tell them
- Morison also agrees with Lake that the women did not at first believe anything supernatural had happened: they just thought Jesus' body had been taken somewhere else

At the end of his book, Morison argues that the man in the tomb was a 'servant of the high priest' who had been in charge of the guards outside the tomb (**Matthew 27: 62-66**). These guards fell asleep at their posts but awoke to find the tomb open and empty. The guards ran back to the city, but high priest's servant stayed behind to investigate.

> *In the closing chapter of his book, Morison offers the charming idea that this 'servant of the high priest' might actually have been the first person to encounter the Risen Jesus.*

The tomb was not visited by the women

This is Morison's final theory. He suggests that it is the only logical alterative to the Resurrection:

> If it could be proved that that grave was not visited on Sunday morning, and that it lay undisturbed and perhaps unthought of for many months afterwards, then the rock upon which all the preceding hypotheses ultimately founder would be removed.

However, in this extract, Morison does not disprove this theory, other than to suggest that it doesn't account for *"what happens afterwards"*.

What does happen afterwards is this: Jesus' disciples become convinced of the Resurrection and go into the streets of Jerusalem, preaching and winning converts. This takes place in a city where:

> *anybody could go and see the tomb between supper and bed-time* – **Frank Morison**

The most prominent Christian apologist today who repeats Morison's arguments is **William Lane Craig**. Craig shares Morison's conclusion that the Disciples would not be able to preach about the Resurrection in Jerusalem if the body was known to be still in the tomb.

Morison concludes that the empty tomb was the one thing the first Christians and their opponents agreed on:

> *We are nowhere told that any responsible person asserted that the body of Jesus was still in the tomb* – **Frank Morison**

He therefore concludes that the women arriving at the correct tomb and found it empty on Easter morning is far more plausible than the idea that the tomb was not visited:

> *However baffling and disconcerting it may seem at first sight, the evidence for the essential accuracy of the women's story is overwhelming in its consistency and strength* – **Frank Morison**

Evaluating Morison's conclusions

A powerful argument that Morison does not consider is that, in the early years of Christianity, there was no interest in visiting Jesus' tomb because the Disciples preached a SPIRITUAL RESURRECTION rather than a bodily Resurrection; i.e. they claimed that Jesus had been raised from the dead as a spiritual being (but his physical body remained dead).

If this is the case, then belief in a bodily Resurrection developed much later, but by then it was too late to track down Jesus' tomb (perhaps because, after 70 CE, the Romans had destroyed it during the siege of Jerusalem).

In support of this, **Paul**'s encounter with the Risen Christ on the road to Damascus (occurring perhaps around 36 CE) seems to be with a spiritual being, not a physical person. The Gospels contain episodes where the Risen Jesus behaves like a spirit (appearing and disappearing, changing his appearance). The examples of the Disciples touching Jesus in **Luke** and **John's Gospel** could have been added in later be the Gospel-writers acting as **redactors** (editors).

There are problems with this interpretation. Jews like the **Pharisees** believed in a bodily Resurrection, whereas Hellenic philosophers supported a spiritual resurrection. You would expect Jesus' earliest followers (who were Jews) to believe in a bodily Resurrection and ideas about spiritual resurrection to creep in over time as more Gentiles join the Church. This is the trend we observe in the **Gospel of Thomas** and the Gnostic texts, which favour a spiritual resurrection and (probably) date from the 2nd century or later.

Morison can also be accused of CHERRY-PICKING: he harmonises the four Gospels into one narrative by selecting details that support his case and ignoring details that don't. For example, Morison omits the scene in **Matthew 28: 2** where the women see an angel come down and roll away the stone blocking the tomb; Morison also interprets the *young man dressed in a white robe* as a flesh-and-blood human, not an angel. He does this because he is a **rationalist** who (in general) prefers naturalistic interpretations to supernatural ones – he makes an exception for the Resurrection itself, but 'explains away' the other supernatural details.

In this, Morison is following **David Hume**'s idea (p16) that even very improbable naturalistic explanations are more likely than supernatural ones. However, he doesn't follow this to Hume's conclusion, which is that no matter how improbable it might be that someone would move Jesus' body and keep it secret, or that Jesus would recover from crucifixion and escape from his tomb, or that the women would visit the wrong tomb, those explanations are still *more probable* than that a dead man rises back to life.

Does Morison make a persuasive case for the Resurrection as a historical fact?

YES	NO
Morison goes through the naturalistic explanations for the empty tomb, methodically, pointing out what is plausible in them but then analyzing the contradictions that come from them. He shows how they contradict the known early history of the Christian Church or ordinary human nature. He is left with the Resurrection as the only remaining hypothesis.	Like a good lawyer, Morison makes the opposing explanations seem weaker than they really are. If Jesus' body was stolen, it doesn't follow that *all* of the Disciples or the Jewish priests were "in on it". The idea of Jesus 'swooning' on the cross is thoroughly discredited but Morison doesn't take seriously the idea that the early Christians might not have preached a bodily Resurrection at all.
Morison is a **rationalist** who doesn't believe in any and all supernatural events. He rejects the descriptions of angels at the tomb and prefers naturalistic interpretations of the *young man in a white robe*. However, when all naturalistic interpretations fail, he is prepared to accept that a miracle has occurred and this is what he concludes about the empty tomb.	Morison respects Hume's advice that *"a wise man proportions his belief to the evidence"* but doesn't follow it through. He cherry-picks his evidence to produce a naturalistic account but then changes his position at the end by proposing a miraculous Resurrection: even improbable naturalistic explanations are more plausible than miracles.

Ian Wilson, *Did Jesus Really Rise from the Dead?*

The Edexcel Anthology includes this passage as extract #9. As with the previous extract, the date is a bit misleading. Wilson's book 'Jesus: The Evidence' was published in 1984 in support of a Channel4 TV series. A new and updated edition was published in 2000.

Ian Wilson (born 1941) is a writer who specialises in religious and historical mysteries. He was a sceptic in his younger years but converted to (Catholic) Christianity as a result of researching the Turin Shroud.

This curious relic has been kept at the Cathedral of John the Baptist in Turin, Italy since the 14th century CE. Legend claims it is the burial shroud Jesus was wrapped in after crucifixion – the same wrapping found neatly folded in the empty tomb by Peter in **Luke 24: 12** and **John 20: 6**.

The Shroud is a linen cloth bearing the image of a man who is alleged to be Jesus. The image on the shroud is faint sepia (brown) but is much clearer in black-and-white negative – this negative discovered in 1898 by an amateur photographer. Radiocarbon dating suggests the Shroud is from the Middle Ages, not the 1st century, but Wilson and others argue that the Shroud is genuine and preserves the real likeness of Jesus.

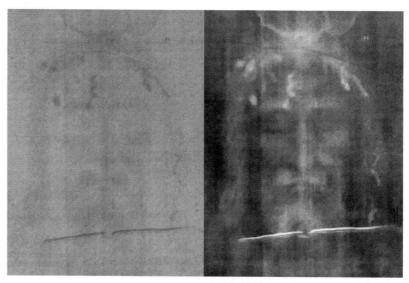

The negative image of the Shroud is striking and shows a man with wounds to his hands and feet, scars on his back and on his brow. No one knows quite how the image was created.

Perhaps because of his association with trying to prove the Shroud of Turin's authenticity, Wilson is not taken very seriously as a New Testament scholar. Wilson doesn't get much praise from conservative Christians either! This seems to be because he's a rationalist who usually prefers naturalistic explanations for the supernatural events in Jesus' life (for example, he speculates that some of Jesus' healings and miracles could be explained if Jesus was a talented hypnotist).

Many of Wilson's religious critics are admiring of **Frank Morison** (p29), despite the fact that both writers have the same rationalist view of the supernatural. The big difference is that Morison is an APOLOGIST: he's defending Christianity and only lines up naturalistic explanations in order to knock them down. Wilson (who wrote his book to accompany a TV documentary) is trying to be fair-minded and balances evidence for the Resurrection with evidence against.

'Jesus: The Evidence' is an attractive 'coffee table' book, full of colour photographs, charts and maps. It takes the reader through the background of Jesus' life and the main arguments. Despite the way 'proper' scholars turn their noses up at it, this book makes a pretty good companion to an A-Level course and students can easily track down second-hand copies for under £3 (including postage).

Identifying the real tomb

The site of the empty tomb is believed to be the modern-day **Church of the Holy Sepulchre** in Jerusalem. Ian Wilson explains why the current church looks nothing like the original tomb: a pagan temple to the goddess Aphrodite had been built on top of it and the site was re-discovered by Helena, wife of Constantine the Great, in the 4th century CE. A combination of Helena's clumsy excavations, the building of a later church on the site and then centuries of warfare over the city between Christians and Muslims means that nothing is now left of the original rock tomb.

There are other contenders for the site of Jesus' tomb. Wilson claims that there are 60 examples of ancient rock tombs in Jerusalem. The 'Garden Tomb' is a popular site for pilgrims because it is relatively untouched, in beautiful surroundings, outside the Damascus Gate of the Old City.

The 'Garden Tomb'

Wilson points out how unusual it was for Jesus to be buried in an empty tomb in which *no one had ever been laid* (**John 19: 41**) since these rock tombs were typically used by several generations of a Jewish family. The dead body would be laid out on a stone bench and then, once it had decomposed, the bones would be stored in a stone box called an ossuary. The tomb would be sealed with a boulder that could weigh up to 2 tons. This closely matches the description of Jesus' tomb in all four Gospels.

Evaluating Wilson's view of the tomb

There are good reasons for Wilson to be suspicious of the Church of the Holy Sepulchre's claim to be the site of the empty tomb. Its discovery by Helena was a 'publicity stunt' on behalf of her husband, the first Christian Roman Emperor. The fragments of the 'True Cross' and the *'titulum'* (the notice originally fixed to the top of the cross identifying Jesus as 'King of the Jews') are widely thought to be fakes.

However, since the Gospels all describe the tomb as being **outside** the city walls, it's odd that Helena should identify a site **inside** the walls of Jerusalem. What Helena couldn't have known is that the walls had been rebuilt since the 1st century and that the site she selected **would have been outside the walls** in 30 CE when Jesus was crucified. This suggests that Helena didn't pick a site at random: she really was guided by a local tradition that this was indeed the genuine location of the empty tomb.

There must, therefore, have been something very compelling about the location for Helena to have ignored the gospels' clear descriptions. As archaeologist Dr Kathleen Kenyon discovered in the 1960s, the Church of the Holy Sepulchre site was outside the city walls of Jesus' time, and would seem to have been within a quarry then being used for burials.

On the other hand, the 'Garden Tomb' has been dated back to the 8th century BCE. This means it could not have been a new and unused tomb when Jesus was buried, as **Matthew** and **John's Gospel** both claim. Most archaeologists support Wilson that there's little evidence to connect the 'Garden Tomb' to Jesus, but it is regarded as the true tomb by some religious groups (such as the Church of Latter Days Saints or 'Mormons').

Discrepancies in the Resurrection accounts

Wilson gives a brief account of the circumstances of Jesus' death and burial and the discovery of the empty tomb. Like **Morison**, he produces a harmonized narrative by bringing details from all the Gospels together. Also like Morison, he rejects the earthquake and angel in **Matthew's** version of the story as *"pious embroideries by an author demonstrably over-fond of the miraculous."*

This is the sort of comment that makes Wilson unpopular with conservative Christians, despite the fact that Morison takes a similar view.

Unlike Morison, Wilson goes on to list the Resurrection appearances themselves, distinguishing those that appear to be spiritual from those that are clearly a bodily resurrection. He also links these appearances to the way the first Christians preached about the Resurrection, as described in the **Book of Acts**.

> *Now I and those with me can witness to everything he did throughout the countryside of Judaea and in Jerusalem itself: and also to the fact that they killed him by hanging him on a tree, yet three days afterwards God raised him to life and allowed him to be seen, not by the whole people, but only by certain witnesses God had chosen beforehand. Now we are those witnesses – we have eaten and drunk with him after his resurrection from the dead ...*
> *(Acts 10: 39–42)*

Wilson dates Paul's belief in the Resurrection to *perhaps as early as 36 AD* [sic] and suggests *"there remains no uncontested rational answer"* to *"the central mystery of the Christian religion"* which is, How did this belief in the Resurrection come about? (Wilson is careful with his words. There is a non-rational answer: the supernatural raising of Jesus from the dead by God.)

Wilson highlights the discrepancies between the Gospel accounts of the Resurrection:

Matthew	Mark	Luke	John
Mary Magdalene is with another Mary	Mary Magdalene is with another Mary and Salome	Mary Magdalene is with another Mary and Joanna	Mary Magdalene arrives alone
An angel opens the tomb	The tomb is open and a young man is inside	The tomb is open and two men/angels appear	The tomb is open is empty
The women tell the Eleven that Jesus has risen and are believed	The women tell no one	The women tell the Eleven that Jesus has risen but are not believed	Mary tells Peter and the 'Beloved Disciple' that the body has been removed
The women meet the Risen Jesus on the way home	The 'longer ending' describes Mary Magdalene meeting the Risen Jesus, but she is not believed by the Eleven	The Risen Jesus appears to two disciples **on the road to Emmaus** but they do not recognise him	Back at the tomb, Mary sees two angels then meets the Risen Jesus, whom she mistakes for a gardener
Jesus appears to the Disciples in Galilee	Jesus appears to the Disciples in Galilee	Jesus appears to the Disciples in Jerusalem	Jesus appears to the Disciples in Jerusalem

Wilson adds two more suspicious details: (1) Mary Magdalene is a poor witness, having been cured of madness by Jesus (she was possessed by 'seven devils'); (2) Paul's account in **1 Corinthians 15: 5-8** has a different order of appearances (with no mention of the women at all).

However, Wilson admits two things in favour of these accounts:

1. They possess *"the same quality as the memories of witnesses after a road accident"* which makes them sound like *"personal and highly confused versions of the same story"*

2. If the accounts were invented, why would the Gospel-writers have made women the prime witnesses, especially since *"women's testimony carried a particularly low weight in Jewish Law"*?

The Risen Jesus appears to Mary Magdalene outside the tomb

Evaluating Wilson on the discrepancies

The speeches in Acts are evidence that the early Christians believed in a bodily Resurrection. However, **Luke-Acts** was not composed until the 70s or 80s CE according to most estimates, so the speeches by **Peter** that are reported may not be authentic (since there are 40-50 years between the original speeches and the Gospel).

Paul's epistles (letters) were written in the 50s CE by someone who knew Peter and the other Disciples personally. They are probably a much better guide to what the first Christians believed, but Paul seems to describe Jesus appearing to him in a vision or as a spirit.

The presence of women as the first witnesses passes the CRITERION OF EMBARRASSMENT since this is not a detail the Gospel-writers would invent if they wanted their story to be believed. Women seem to have been very influential at the beginning of Christianity. Wilson implies that Paul misses out the women from his list of Resurrection appearances out of sheer sexism, but that doesn't fit well with Paul's dealings with Christian women leaders like **Lydia** and **Chloe**; Paul entrusts his Epistle to the Romans to **Phoebe**, who delivers to Rome on his behalf – not the behaviour of someone *"for whom women didn't count."*

Frank Morison (p29) suggests a different explanation for these contradictions, which is that the early Christians were accused of stealing Jesus' body themselves. This made it embarrassing for them to admit that the women, Peter and the others had visited the tomb on Easter morning because this would strengthen the accusations that they had carried out a hoax. Therefore, they downplayed the empty tomb and the testimony of the women, which is why, when the Gospel-writers came to record the events years later, the precise details had become confused.

The Six Basic Hypotheses

Just like **Frank Morison** on the empty tomb (p29), Wilson outlines six possible explanations for the Resurrection appearances:

1. **The women went to the wrong tomb**

   Wilson dismisses this in the same way as **Morison** and **Craig**: "*it would have been an easy matter for any sceptic to go to the right location, show the body still there and set the whole matter at rest*".

2. **Someone removed Jesus' body**

   As pointed out by Morison, Wilson argues that once the Disciples started preaching the Resurrection, "*we might surely have expected someone, some time, to produce it*".

3. **The disciples removed Jesus' body**

   Wilson doesn't treat the Theft Hypothesis separately, but seems to regard it as inevitable that, if a follower of Jesus had taken the body, that person would at some point have confessed to what they had done (perhaps because of the persecution they faced).

4. **The Risen Jesus was a hallucination**

   Wilson is dubious about hallucinations that could feel so real to so many people but his main argument is that the Hallucination Hypothesis does not explain the empty tomb.

5. **Jesus survived crucifixion**

   Wilson mentions versions of the Swoon Hypothesis by **Hugh Schonfield, D.H. Lawrence** and **Barbara Thiering**, but refutes them all with **David Strauss'** famous comment that "*a being who had stolen half dead out of the sepulchre*" could not have convinced the Disciples that he was really "*the Prince of Life*".

6. **Jesus really did rise from the dead**

   Wilson suggests this is the most persuasive hypothesis. In support, he describes the transformation of "*the previously denying and demoralized*" Peter into a confident and passionate missionary. He also cites **Edwin Yamauchi** in support of the idea that Paul listing so many witnesses to the Resurrection who were alive at the time he wrote is strong evidence that "*something like* [the Resurrection] *actually happened.*"

> *Wilson maintains a cautious tone, saying only that "something like" the Resurrection happened though we can't know "what exactly happened". This is Wilson being a careful historian and appearing open-minded.*

Wilson offers another criticism, which is that the Gospels were specifically written to counter some of these hypotheses.

1. **Wrong tomb:** The Synoptic Gospels all make a point of mentioning that the women took careful note of where Jesus was buried

2. **Theft of the body:** John's Gospel has Mary Magdalene believing someone has stolen the body
3. **Hoax by the Disciples:** Matthew's Gospel specifically accuses the Jewish leaders of spreading this rumour
4. **Hallucination:** Luke and John's Gospel include scenes where the Disciples are disbelieving until they touch Jesus' hands and feet

If these were standard criticisms leveled at the earliest Christians for their beliefs, then the Gospel-writers might have added these details in purely to answer their critics. This is an example of **Redaction Criticism**: the Gospel-writers edit their material to address problems in their own time rather than to describe what really happened on the first Easter morning.

Wilson concludes by surveying the immense impact of the Resurrection on the lives of the early Christians. He gives the example of Stephen the Martyr and Jesus' own family (such as his brother James) who faced torture and ugly death *"with astonishing cheerfulness, totally confident that what they professed was truth"*:

> . What cannot be emphasized enough is that those who made such claims had absolutely no expectation of any material gain for their outspokenness. Their reward instead, as the following decades and centuries would demonstrate, was all too frequently to be faced with some form of violent death, from being stoned, to being torn to pieces by wild animals in a Roman arena, to being crucified in some yet more grotesque and painful manner.

The last remark is a reference to Peter's fate: he was executed in Rome, crucified upside down.

Evaluating Wilson on the Six Basic Hypotheses

Wilson's hypotheses are essentially the same as **Morison**'s (although he adds the Hallucination Theory) and have already been evaluated. His treatment of the Theft Hypothesis is perhaps too brief. When the Disciples started preaching Jesus' Resurrection in public, it was 7 weeks after the Crucifixion according to **Luke-Acts**, which would have made it impossible for anyone to produce a recognisable corpse to refute these claims. It is also at least *possible* that some Disciple died without telling anyone that the Resurrection had been a hoax.

Wilson describes some pretty sensationalist versions of the Swoon Theory – but this is because his book accompanied a TV documentary that tried to catch the viewers' attention with weird ideas. **Barbara Thiering**'s theory is worth a bit more consideration.

Thiering is an Australian scholar whose book *Jesus, The Man* (1992) offers a radical reinterpretation of Jesus' life story. Thiering thinks that Jesus was an **Essene** and that the Gospels are all written in code. According to the way Thiering decodes' the New Testament, Jesus married twice, had four children and died of old age in Rome around 60 CE.

Thiering's ideas are rejected by other scholars but they demonstrate that, with a bit of imagination, the Gospels can be interpreted in *very* unusual ways.

The idea that the transformation of **Peter** and the other Disciples proves that the Resurrection (or *something like it*) happened is a weak argument. We don't know much about what Peter was like **before** the Resurrection, because the Gospels focus more on Jesus than his Disciples' personalities.

Perhaps Peter had always been charismatic and confident and a dazzling public speaker and just needed an opportunity to step out from under Jesus' shadow!

Even if Peter did transform from a cowardly nobody into an amazing preacher, this doesn't prove his Resurrection experience was objectively real, only that Peter and the others **believed** it was real.

It's not unusual for people to 'reinvent' themselves after a breakdown or a life crisis and this might be what happened to Peter, Paul, Stephen and the others. The fact that belief in the Resurrection was psychologically good for Peter and the rest doesn't make it automatically true.

Peter is a spiritual hero to most Christians and Catholics view him as the first Pope

The theory that the Gospel-writers **redacted** details into their accounts to refute criticisms by unbelievers is unprovable. However, it can be shown to be unlikely if there were other naturalistic explanations of the Resurrection which the Gospels do **not** make a point of refuting in this way.

One such hypothesis that Wilson does not consider is the SUBSTITUTION HYPOTHESIS: Jesus was replaced on the cross by a substitute who looked just like him, perhaps even his identical twin brother. This is not a modern idea but is present in 2nd and 3rd century texts like *The Acts of Thomas* (the Disciple Thomas being Jesus' twin, since 'Thomas' is Greek for 'twin').

However, the Gospels don't make a point of refuting the Substitution Hypothesis (e.g. by making it clear Jesus didn't have any twin brothers). The Gospel-writers would surely do this if they were redacting material just to refute all the popular criticisms of the Resurrection that were going around.

Wilson's conclusion is that the rapid spread of Christianity was unusual despite great opposition and *"something very powerful had fired them into such resoluteness of belief."* Wilson is not trying to prove the Resurrection happened so much as encourage his readers to view the matter more open-mindedly before arriving at their own conclusions.

Does Morison make a persuasive case for the Resurrection as a historical fact?

YES	NO
Wilson argues that the **Church of the Holy Sepulchre** probably is the true site of the empty tomb and that the transformation in the lives of **Peter** and other disciples is best explained by the fact of the Resurrection. He demonstrates that naturalistic alternatives to the Resurrection are all flawed.	Wilson makes an equally persuasive case *against* the Resurrection, pointing out that the Gospels were redacted to refute early criticisms of the Resurrection, which makes them poor sources of evidence in favour of it, and that the accounts of the Resurrection are full of discrepancies and contradictions.
Wilson is trying to be fair-minded by presenting arguments for-and-against but his arguments 'for' are stronger. He presents the 'Six Basic Hypotheses' as already refuted by **David Strauss** except for the sixth, which is that the Resurrection happened. The biggest section of the extract concentrates on the transformation of the early Christian believers into fearless martyrs, which is best explained by an experience of Jesus rising from the dead.	Wilson devotes too much time on the weakest of the 'Six Basic Hypotheses' (#5, Swoon Theory) but doesn't give enough serious consideration to the stronger ones (that the body of Jesus was stolen) and gives no consideration at all to the idea that the Disciples originally believed in a spiritual Resurrection, not a bodily one. He is too willing to believe that, because the Disciples were empowered by their belief in the Resurrection, something like it must have happened.

TOPIC 6.2 HOW SHOULD WE LIVE?

Christianity is not just a set of theological beliefs about Jesus and the Resurrection; it is a body of ethical codes for a moral life. Jesus' ministry seems to be a mixture of **eschatological** warnings (about the end of the world) and moral teachings along with **miracles and Signs** (which may have eschatological or ethical hidden meanings).

One of the most distinctive features of Jesus' teachings in the Synoptic Gospels (especially **Luke's Gospel**) is his use of **Parables**. These are short stories, normally rooted in the everyday life of Palestinian farmers but sometimes based on familiar folk tales. Parables have one or more hidden meanings – sometimes eschatological (related to the end of the world or the afterlife), sometimes moral, often both.

Another highlight in Jesus' teaching is the sermon reported in **Matthew** and **Luke's Gospel**. The 'Sermon on the Mount' takes up **Matthew 5-7.** The mountain setting emphasizes Jesus' role as the 'new Moses' in Matthew's Gospel (since **Moses** received the **Law** from God on Mount Sinai). This Sermon includes the famous 'Beatitudes' (blessings) and the 'Lord's Prayer' and is considered to be the core of Christian teachings.

The 'Sermon on the Plain' in **Luke 6** is shorter but contains some similar material and will be considered in detail on p53.

1st century Judaism

Jesus' ethical teaching used to be considered utterly distinctive with its focus on love and forgiveness. However, scholars argue that much of Jesus' preaching is based on Jewish morality contained in the Old Testament.

For example, a central teaching of Jesus is 'love your neighbour' (e.g. **Mark 12: 31**) but this also appears in the Old Testament:

> *You shall not take vengeance, nor bear any grudge against the sons of your people, but you shall love your neighbor as yourself* – **Leviticus 19: 18**

Rather than proposing a brand new moral code, Jesus seems to have taken the traditional Jewish moral code and refocused it:

- Jesus taught that morality should not just be about external behaviour, but internal thoughts and feelings, so that lust is just as bad as adultery
- Jesus was a moral perfectionist, arguing that people should aim for the highest possible standards in their lives; he held particularly high standards on marriage and divorce
- Jesus criticised the Jewish purity laws (such as ceremonial washing and keeping the Sabbath), arguing that moral behaviour was more important than purity

Jesus argued that he did not come to replace the laws in the Old Testament, but to give them their correct interpretation:

> *Do not think that I have come to abolish the Law or the Prophets; I have not come to abolish them but to fulfill them* – **Matthew 5: 17**

As usual with the Gospels, it's hard to tell if Jesus is making an ethical statement (fulfilling the Scriptures through his moral teachings) or an eschatological statement (fulfilling them through dying an atoning death).

Christian codes of living

The early Church took Jesus' teachings and applied them in the light of Hellenic ethical theories like Stoicism. Stoicism (which was the major philosophical system of the Roman Empire) urged people to show self-control and resist passions. Stoic ethics are an influence on Paul' epistles (letters) which became guides for Christians:

> *Let us behave decently, as in the daytime, not in carousing and drunkenness, not in sexual immorality and debauchery, not in dissension and jealousy* – **Romans 13: 13**

This focus on CONTINENCE (controlling the passions and bodily urges) led to a distinctive Christian emphasis on virginity and a powerful sense of sex as being sinful. Christian churches still promote CELIBACY (rejecting sexual relationships) and CHASTITY (restricting sex solely to married partners). Other forms of sex are condemned as the sin of FORNICATION. This pessimistic view of sex is **not** directly based on Jesus' teaching or on Judaism generally (which tends to view sex as a positive thing, although the **Essenes** seem to have taken vows of celibacy).

A related teaching is the condemnation of homosexuality as the sin of SODOMY. This is clearly a teaching adapted from Judaism, since the Old Testament threatens homosexuality with severe punishments.

However, a crucial Christian teaching is stated by **Augustine of Hippo** (354-430 CE): *Cum dilectione hominum et odio vitiorum* is translated as:

Love the sinner and hate the sin – **Augustine**

In other words, although Christians condemn homosexual or promiscuous BEHAVIOUR, they should continue to love and respect the PERSON.

Another distinctive moral teaching among early Christians was the sharing of property (COMMUNAL OWNERSHIP). The **Book of Acts** describes converts to Christianity selling their houses and land and donating the money to the Christian community so that *"there were no needy persons among them."*

No one claimed that any of their possessions was their own, but they shared everything they had – **Acts 4: 32**

This practice seems to have faded from the Church as belief in an imminent *Parousia* ('Second Coming' of Jesus) was replaced by a belief in a delayed *Parousia* (a change in belief that scholars claim is shown in **Luke's Gospel**).

However, a new movement replaced communal ownership, which was MONASTICISM. Christians like **Anthony of Egypt** (251-356 CE) would escape from life in the pagan cities to live as hermits in the desert.

These hermits were known as ANCHORITES and over time they started living together in small communities, taking vows of celibacy and sharing property in common like the first Christians. In Europe, they are known as MONKS and their places of retreat are called monasteries.

St Catherine's monastery, Mount Sinai in Egypt: one of the oldest Christian monasteries in the world (founded in the 6th century CE)

This practice has little in common with Judaism (which encourages Jews to be productive members of society), but the **Essenes** lived in desert monasteries and Jesus advised his followers to give up their possessions:

> *If you want to be perfect, go, sell your possessions and give to the poor, and you will have treasure in heaven* – **Matthew 19: 21**

This advice continues to be divisive, with some Christians believing Jesus commands 'holy poverty' – such as **Francis of Assisi** (1181-1226 CE) who gave up everything he owned.

Other Christians argue for AFFECTIVE POVERTY, which means being detached from caring about wealth but still using wealth to do good in the world.

> *Spelling matters. Affective (with an 'a') means 'emotional'; effective (with an 'e') means having consequences. Effective poverty is literally owning nothing but affective poverty means that money doesn't matter to you emotionally.*

Equality today

A distinctive Christian insight is the **equality** of all people before God:

- God loves all persons equally (*"God does not show favouritism"* – **Romans 2: 13**)
- All persons are equally sinners and all need God's forgiveness and mercy (*"all have sinned and fall short of the glory of God"* – **Romans 3: 23**)

This is linked to the central Christian teaching of mutual love (*agape* in Greek, meaning selfless compassion for all people). Jesus gives this final teaching to his Disciples:

> *A new command I give you: Love one another. As I have loved you, so you must love one another* – **John 13: 34**

An early Christian scholar named **Tertullian** (160-230 CE) quotes the Roman pagans as saying *"See how these Christians love one another!"* because they were so struck by the equality and charity in Christian communities.

However, Christians have often failed to put this EGALITARIANISM (philosophy of equality) into practice

- **Slavery:** Jesus did not comment on slavery in the Roman Empire. **Paul**'s Christian converts included slaves and he advised them to obey their masters (**Ephesians 6: 5**). Paul's epistle (letter) to **Philemon** concerns a runaway slave whom Paul has converted to Christianity; Paul writes to the Christian master asking him to forgive the slave but does not ask him to *free* the slave.

    In the 18th century, Christian abolitionists like the **Quakers** and **Methodists** successfully banned slavery in Britain, but other Christians opposed them at the time with Biblical arguments. Today, all Christian churches oppose slavery.

- **Women:** The first Christian churches seem to have been led by women like Lydia, Priscilla, Chloe and Phoebe who are mentioned in **Acts** and in **Paul's epistles**. Christianity seems to have been popular with women, because it allowed them to preach, it promoted celibacy (which meant women converts didn't have to marry and fall under the authority of a husband) and it opposed the Hellenic practice of abandoning unwanted baby daughters to die.

  However, the Church quickly acquired the sexist gender roles of the Roman Empire and later New Testament texts forbid women to teach or even to speak in church. The **Catholic Church** continues to refuse women priests, although other churches are changing in this regard: the **Church of England** ordained its first female priest in 1994 and first female bishop in 2014.

- **Antisemitism:** Hostility towards the Jews is rooted in the experiences of the 1st century Christians, who blamed the Jewish leaders for the crucifixion of Jesus and experienced some persecution from the Jewish authorities. This hostility is particularly evident in the **Gospel of John**, which lays the foundation for centuries of Christian antisemitism.

  Once Christianity became the main religion in the Roman Empire, Jewish communities suffered attacks and legal restrictions (such as refusal of permission to build or repair their Synagogues).

  In the Middle Ages, European Jews were forbidden to own land and were forced to work as moneylenders; they were subjected to attacks and were expelled from many countries (England in 1290 CE, Spain in 1492 CE, and many others). Jewish communities were forced to live in ghettos, identify themselves with special clothing and were subjected to 'pogroms' (genocides). Many Christian churches today have apologised for supporting these atrocities: the Catholic Church condemned antisemitism in 2015.

In the 21st century, Christianity faces challenges for how the principle of equality should be applied to new groups that have previously been ignored, such as the LGBTQ+ community.

Pluralism today

Pluralism is the idea of many truths – or many approaches to the truth. The early Christians lived in a pluralistic Roman Empire, where people followed a variety of philosophies and worshipped different gods and goddesses without necessarily regarding the others as 'false'. However, Christianity followed the Jewish teaching of their being only one God, with all the other pagan deities being either idols (mere statues with no reality behind them) or else demons.

Christianity made EXCLUSIVE claims right from the start, teaching that salvation *only* comes through accepting Jesus as Lord. The first preaching by **Peter** concerning Jesus claims that "*salvation is found in no one else*" (**Acts 4: 12**); this links to Jesus' own statement:

> *I am the way and the truth and the life. No one comes to the Father except through me –*
> **John 14: 6**

Christianity continued to be an EXCLUSIVIST religion through the Middle Ages, with examples of some people (e.g. the pagan Lithuanians) being forced to convert to Christianity at sword point and heretical movements (such as the Cathars in southern France) targeted by military reprisals.

When Christianity split into Protestant and Catholic factions during the Reformation, these groups maintained exclusivist views and fought against each other in particularly bloody wars through to the 17th century.

However, the sheer brutality of these wars produced a counter-response: the ECUMENICAL MOVEMENT looks for common ground between Catholics and Protestants, focusing on the beliefs they share and encouraging them to worship together.

One response to this was the institution of RELIGIOUS LIBERTY: the freedom of individuals to follow whichever religion they choose without fear of punishment or persecution. This is a particularly important principle in the Constitution of the USA. It is linked to the idea of RELIGIOUS TOLERATION: the obligation on all religions to coexist peacefully with different faiths.

At first, liberty and toleration were ideas applied to different Christian churches, then to Jewish minority populations in Christian countries and atheists. However, mass immigration in the 19th and 20th centuries introduced the demand for the liberty and toleration of non-Judeo-Christian religions, such as Hinduism, Islam and Sikhism.

In the 20th century, many scholars encouraged the idea of RELIGIOUS PLURALISM: that all or most religions **worship the same God** despite expressing themselves with different imagery, myths and terminology. There are broadly two responses to this:

- LIBERAL scholars encourage religious pluralism, which means downplaying or abandoning exclusivist teachings. **John Hick** is a famous Christian pluralist; **Dietrich Bonhoeffer** argues for "*religionless Christianity*" and **Rudolf Bultmann**'s de-mythologized Christianity is a way of interpreting the Bible for a pluralist society. This approach sees Christianity as just one religious path among many and Jesus as not necessarily superior to other religious founders like the Buddha or Muhammad.

  there is a deep devotion to God, true sainthood, and deep spiritual life within these other religions – **John Hick**

- CONSERVATIVE scholars reject religious pluralism as taking religious liberty and toleration too far. They argue that religious pluralism undermines the essential truth claims of Christianity (e.g. that Jesus is the Son of God and the only way to salvation) and point out that religious pluralism also disrespects other religions too by undermining **their** distinctive truth claims (e.g. that Muhammad is the last and greatest prophet and that the Qur'an is God's definitive revelation).

  it is comforting to pretend that the great religions make up one big, happy family. But this sentiment, however well-intentioned, is neither accurate nor ethically responsible – **Stephen Prothero**

The Sermon on the Plain in Luke 6

Luke describes Jesus' memorable sermon as happening on *a level place* after Jesus has descended from a mountaintop. Scholars debate whether this is the same Sermon that **Matthew's Gospel** describes happening on a mountain (in which case it may be from the **Q-source**) or a different sermon with a similar theme.

A difference between the two sermons is that Matthew's 'Sermon on the Mount' focuses on Jesus' Disciples and teaches them how to live as righteous Jews, Luke's 'Sermon on the Plain' has more of a focus on topics that would interest Gentiles as well as Jews.

Frank J. Matera argues that Matthew's 'Sermon on the Mount' is *"to show that Jesus did not come to abolish the Law and the Prophets but to fulfil them"* whereas Luke's 'Sermon on the Plain' *"focuses on the need to extend love to all, even to one's enemy"*.

> *It's a bit odd that the Exam Board expects you to know this passage well enough to answer on it, but doesn't include it as an extract in the Anthology.*

The Beatitudes ('Blessings') – Luke 6: 20-23

In both sermons, Jesus blesses his Disciples. Each blessing identifies a particular type of unhappiness *now* and promises a *future* reward or consolation.

> Blessed are you who are poor,
>
>> for yours is the kingdom of God.
>
> 21 Blessed are you who hunger now,
>
>> for you will be satisfied.
>
> Blessed are you who weep now,
>
>> for you will laugh.
>
> 22 Blessed are you when people hate you,
>
> when they exclude you and insult you
>
> and reject your name as evil,
>
>> because of the Son of Man.

There are four blessings here: for the poor, the hungry, the weeping and the persecuted.

1. **The Poor:** This is the idea that poverty is a blessed state. The Christian idea of poverty is rather contradictory: the poor are blessed yet Christians are commanded by Jesus to give their money to the poor to relieve their poverty.

Poverty is blessed because the poor, having nothing else, are able to depend entirely on God, whereas the rich are tempted to cling to the illusory comforts of their possessions. Luke makes the same point in the **Parable of the Sower** (c.f. **Topic 5.1 Kingdom of God**) where the *good seed* is choked by *thorns* which represent worldly possessions and commitments.

In Matthew's version this is also the first blessing but Matthew makes this meaning clearer by writing *"blessed are the poor in spirit"* to show that it is the spiritual impact of poverty, rather than the brute fact of having no money, that enables the poor to live within the **Kingdom of God**. This is the basis for affective poverty, which is trying to live *as is* you were poor in order to make room for God in your life.

2. **The Hungry:** Hunger is linked to poverty and Christians are expected to end hunger through charitable giving. However, Jesus' promise that the hungry will be *satisfied* is also an eschatological promise: it refers to the Afterlife or to the Kingdom of God on earth when God rules and everyone is treated fairly.

   There is a link here to the **Parable of the Banquet** (c.f. **Topic 5.1**) and the **Sign of the Feeding of the 5000** (c.f. **Topic 2.3**) as well as Jesus describing himself as the **Bread of Life** (c.f. **Topic 2.2**). When Jesus talks about food, he is often speaking symbolically: the hunger is a spiritual hunger and the food is himself; this spiritual food is received through Jesus' teachings but also in the **Eucharist** ceremony when Christians share bread in memory of Jesus' atoning death.

   Once again, Matthew's version of the sermon spiritualizes this blessing, writing *"blessed are those who hunger and thirst for righteousness"* which makes the symbolic meaning clearer.

> *Did the Beatitudes start out as spiritual blessings which Luke has transformed into social morality (literal poverty and hunger) or did they start off as social morality which Matthew then spiritualizes into something more allegorical?*

3. **The Weeping:** Those who *weep* refers to all human misery, but particularly people mourning for the dead. Matthew's version makes this the second blessing and explicitly refers to *"blessed are those who mourn"*.

   There is an instruction here to comfort the unhappy people, but there are also links to occasions when Jesus describes the **Kingdom of God** as being like a party, with everybody celebrating (for example, the **Parable of the Banquet** or the **Sign of Turning Water into Wine**). There is an eschatological promise here that the sufferings of this world will come to an end.

   On another level, the blessing refers to the **Resurrection**: those who weep are the Disciples themselves, after the Crucifixion, but they will laugh again when Jesus is raised from the dead.

4. **The Persecuted:** Those who are hated, excluded, insulted and rejected are the future Christians (this is the only blessing that does not use the word *now*). Jesus adds that they should *"leap for joy"* when they are persecuted for their faith because it shows that they are his true followers, just like *the prophets* who were also persecuted by the Jews.

Of course, the later Christians **were** persecuted in various ways by the Jewish and Roman authorities (these persecutions were perhaps still happening while Luke's Gospel was being written). Some Christians abandoned their faith, going back to their pagan or Jewish communities. This links to the **Parable of the Sower** where the good seed that produces a harvest is the one that *perseveres*.

1st century Judaism: There are strong links from the Beatitudes back to the Jewish Scriptures. For example, **Psalm 41** begins with a blessing for those who watch out for the poor and are kind to the weak; **Psalm 107** promises that God will *fill the hungry soul*; **Isaiah 61: 2** promises that God will comfort those who mourn and the Jewish experience of mourning for their lost homeland during the Babylonian Exile (586-538 BCE) gave mourning and weeping a spiritual significance in Judaism too.

Christian codes of living: The Christian duty to give to the poor, feed the hungry, comfort the unhappy and to bear suffering cheerfully is summed up here. In Anthology extract #9, **Ian Wilson** (p38) comments on how the early Christians took the message to heart when they faced martyrdom *"with an astonishing cheerfulness"*. Religious reformers like **Francis of Assisi** have been inspired by the Beatitudes: Francis gave up all his possessions, exchanged his clothes with a beggar's rags and lived entirely dependent on God for food and shelter, living as a 'holy fool'. Francis composed the beautiful *Canticle of the Sun*, in which he praises Brother Sun and Sister Moon even Sister Death, while he was suffering from an eye disease that caused him unspeakable pain and left him nearly blind.

Equality today: The Beatitudes have been criticised by political reformers because they appear to be promising believers 'pie in the sky' as a consolation for putting up with injustice in the world. However, many Christians interpret the Beatitudes as a 'call to arms' instead: poverty, hunger and misery are things that God expects humans to confront and deal with. These Christians see the promise at the end of each blessing as something **we humans** are supposed to achieve in **this** life, not something that God brings about in the Afterlife. Much of the world's poverty, hunger and misery is linked to inequality of wealth and opportunity so Christians follow Jesus' example by challenging the powerful on behalf of the weak and the helpless.

Pluralism today: In 2016, **Pope Francis** preached a sermon on the Beatitudes and offered 6 more to *"recognise and respond to new situations with fresh energy"*:

- Blessed are those who remain faithful while enduring evils inflicted on them by others, and forgive them from their heart
- Blessed are those who look into the eyes of the abandoned and marginalized, and show them their closeness
- Blessed are those who see God in every person, and strive to make others also discover him

- Blessed are those who protect and care for our common home
- Blessed are those who renounce their own comfort in order to help others
- Blessed are those who pray and work for full communion between Christians

The last of Pope Francis' beatitudes is a clear reference to ECUMENISM (the coming together of different Christian churches). The reference to *"those who see God in every person,"* *"who protect and are for our current home"* (the environment) and *"who renounce their own comfort to help others"* also links to RELIGIOUS PLURALISM, because such people do not have to be Catholics or even Christians.

The Four Woes – Luke 6: 24-26

The next section occurs only in Luke's version of the sermon (but similar warnings directed against the **Pharisees** are in **Matthew 23:1–39**). Jesus pronounces four *'woes'* (literally *'sorrows'* but here meaning *'warnings'*) for different groups of people. These *'woes'* are the mirror-image of the Beatitudes, describing people who are happy and contended *now* and threatening dreadful things for them in the future.

> [24] 'But woe to you who are rich,
>
> for you have already received your comfort.
>
> [25] Woe to you who are well fed now,
>
> for you will go hungry.
>
> Woe to you who laugh now,
>
> for you will mourn and weep.
>
> [26] Woe to you when everyone speaks well of you,
>
> for that is how their ancestors treated the false prophets.

1. **The Rich:** The reference to the rich *receiving their comfort* in the here-and-now is echoed in the **Parable of the Rich Man & Lazarus** (p76), which would make this an eschatological warning about events at the end of the world or in the Afterlife. This also links to **The Rich & The Kingdom of God** (c.f. **Topic 5.1**) and its simile of a camel going through the eye of a needle (**Luke 18: 18-30**). The underlying idea is that the pleasures of wealth are short-term and fleeting, but the pains of Hell last forever.
2. **The Well-Fed:** These people will *go hungry* in future. This also links to the **Parable of the Rich Man & Lazarus** (p76), suggesting God's punishment on those who feed themselves rather than caring about the needs of others. *Going hungry* could be another eschatological warning about Hell. However, a symbolic interpretation would be that the *well-fed* are people who do not recognise their spiritual needs and satisfy themselves with worldly pleasures instead: they will *go hungry* because they will be spiritually empty.

3. **The Laughers:** These people will *mourn and weep*. Luke's Gospel describes Jesus being laughed at and mocked by the Jewish rulers, the soldiers and the other crucified thieves. The 'laughers' are also the people who insult and sneer at the future Christians – people like the pagan critic **Celsus** who describes Christianity as appealing only to *"the silly, and the mean, and the stupid, with slaves, women and children."* This eschatological warning suggests that these critics won't be laughing on Judgement Day! However, more generally, the 'laughers' are people who live only for pleasure and the present moment who, like the rich, have chosen temporary pleasures and an eternity in Hell.

4. **The False Prophets:** These are the people who are *well spoken of* and Jesus compares them to *"false prophets"*. In the later Church, these people are the heretics who attract crowds of fans with distorted versions of the Christian message. Conservative Christians today would link this warning to liberal Christians who produce 'watered down' versions of Christianity that are acceptable to atheists.

1st century Judaism: There is a criticism here of the Jews whose ancestors *spoke well of false prophets* just as they persecuted the true prophets. The prophets the Jews are supposed to have killed are **Isaiah** (sawed in half, according to tradition) and **Jeremiah** (cause of death unknown). The *false prophets* refer the priests of pagan gods like Baal that the Israelites went over to worshiping in the past. By condemning the ancestors of the Jewish leaders, Jesus is condemning the religious traditions of the **Pharisees** and the **Sadducees** as misguided.

Christian codes of living: The condemnation of the 'Laughers' invites later Christians to CENSOR writing and performances that use satirical humour to attack Christian beliefs. Recent examples of this include: *Monty Python's Life of Brian* (1979), which was banned in several cities and countries (Ireland and Norway!), picketed by protesting Christians and accused of blasphemy; *Jerry Springer – The Opera*, which was shown on the BBC in 2005 and drew 55,000 complaints for its representations of Jesus. More recent satirists who have attacked Christianity include Ricky Gervais, Bill Maher and Trey Parker/Matt Stone (creators of *South Park* and the musical *The Book of Mormon*).

Equality today: The 'woes' threatened to the 'Rich' and the 'Well-Fed' inspire Christian activism against powerful and privileged groups. Christian thinkers are also coming to see how these categories represent *everyone* in Western countries: we are all, collectively, *wealthy* and *well-fed* compared to the developing economies and therefore are condemned by Jesus too unless we can contribute to making the world a fairer place.

Pluralism today: The concept of *false prophets* has been very divisive in Christianity. Alternative interpretations of Jesus' teachings were treated as HERESIES and some of them were crushed with extreme violence (such as the Cathar heresy in the South of France in the 13th century CE). Later Christians developed the idea of the '**Antichrist**': a servant of the Devil who would lead people astray and persecute true Christians. For centuries, Protestants have viewed the Catholic Pope as 'antichrist' but throughout history the title has been awarded to the Emperor Nero, Napoleon Bonaparte and Barack Obama!

Loving Your Enemies – Luke 6: 27-36

This passage is similar to **Matthew 5: 43-48** but uses different terminology and examples. Jesus sums up his teaching at the start:

> *love your enemies, do good to those who hate you* **– Luke 6: 27**

Jesus gives a series of illustrations of this teaching in action:

- If you are slapped, *turn the other cheek* (so that that cheek can be slapped too)
- If someone takes your coat, give them your shirt too
- Don't ask for something back if someone takes it

These instructions go beyond the normal 'law of reciprocity' (which says, treat other people the way they treat you) and amounts to a sort of radical altruism (treat other people well *regardless* of how they treat you). Jesus sums up again at the end:

> *love your enemies, do good to them, and lend to them without expecting to get anything back* **– Luke 6: 35**

These recommendations are 'counsels of perfection' and are often criticised for being too idealistic and unworldly. However, Jesus shows a shrewd grasp of psychology when he points out that even *sinners* have friends whom they treat well (e.g. Hitler loved his dog!). The fact that you are nice to the people who are nice to you really reveals very little about your character: the mark of a moral person is that you behave well towards the people who are *not* nice to you.

In this passage, Jesus states the 'Golden Rule' of ethics:

> *Do to others as you would have them do to you* **– Luke 6: 31**

Again, this goes beyond the 'law of reciprocity' (which says, treat other people *exactly* the way they treat you) and amounts to something more radical (treat other people the way you'd like to be treated, *regardless* of how they treat you).

Jesus himself lives out this code: during his trial he is slapped by the priests and the soldiers, during the Crucifixion the guards divide his clothes between them, **Luke 23: 34** describes Jesus praying for his enemies from the cross.

1st century Judaism: The Jewish Scriptures also contain instructions to love your enemy so Jesus is not deviating from Jewish ethics here. **Exodus 23: 4-5** contains instructions to return an enemy's livestock and **Proverbs 24: 17-18** advises Jews not to rejoice when their enemies suffer. However, there are also verses that counsel the law of reciprocity, such as the famous *"eye for an eye"* instruction (**Leviticus 24: 20**, known as the *lex talionis* or 'law of retaliation'). Jesus is clarifying the Scriptures and offering a definitive interpretation.

Jesus also goes beyond standard Jewish ethical advice. The famous Jewish teacher **Hillel the Elder** (110 BCE – 10 CE) summed up the ethics in the Torah as: *"What is hateful to you, do not do to your fellow."*

However, this is a NEGATIVE formulation (saying ***don't*** treat others the way you'd hate to be treated yourself) whereas Jesus' formulation is POSITIVE (***do*** treat others the way you'd ideally like to be treated yourself). Jesus' version of the Golden Rule is an ethical advance on previous versions.

Christian codes of living: The first Christians (and perhaps Jesus himself) were APOCALYPTICISTS: they believed in an imminent end of the world. Therefore, incredibly demanding ethical rules about submitting to injustice, not retaliating and giving away your possessions would only have to be followed for a short time. Later Christians came to understand that *Parousia* (Jesus' 'Second Coming') had been delayed and settled into the 'long haul' of history with a less extreme ethical code. For example, **Augustine of Hippo** (410 CE) set out the conditions for a 'Just War' under which Christians were morally allowed to retaliate against their enemies. Nonetheless, Christian martyrs really did follow Jesus' original advice, going to their torture and death without resisting and forgiving their enemies.

Later protestors adapted the tactic of PASSIVE RESISTANCE from Jesus' teachings. For example, **Gandhi** used this technique in India and **Martin Luther King** used it in the USA. Gandhi was a Hindu, but called Jesus *"the most active resister known perhaps to history... non-violence par excellence"* (1948). King explained his non-violent protests against racism: *"the Christian doctrine of love operating through the Gandhian method of nonviolence was one of the most potent weapons available to oppressed people in their struggle for freedom"* (1959).

Equality today: Since every person desires to be treated as an equal by others, the Golden Rule states that we must treat others as equals, even if they are enemies (perhaps, for Christians, ***especially*** if they are enemies). There are implications here for the 21st century in which homosexual couples demand equal rights to marry and transgender persons demand equal respect as members of their self-identified gender. Conservative Christians who argue that these equal statuses should ***not*** be granted have to explain why the Golden Rule need not apply in these cases.

For example, in 2014 a family-run bakery in Northern Ireland refused to make a cake with a slogan supporting same-sex marriage because it opposed their religious beliefs about marriage; they were prosecuted by the Equalities Commission and fined for discrimination. Similar cases are being tried in the USA with similar results: equality laws mean that religious principles do not justify discrimination.

Pluralism today: The Golden Rule supports religious liberty and religious toleration, even toleration of religions that some Christians might consider to be their 'enemies'. However, this raises questions about how far tolerance should go, as has been seen in debates about faith schools, religious dress codes and extremist violence.

For example, in 2017 a terrorist bomb outside an Egyptian Cathedral killed 47 Christians celebrating Easter; the widow of one of the victims forgave the ISIS-inspired attacker, saying: *"I'm not angry at the one who did this, I am telling him, may God forgive you."* However, even when individuals choose to react this way, the state still has an obligation to punish terrorists and prevent future attacks. Augustine's argument that circumstances justify Christians using force against enemies could also justify restricting the rights of extremist groups in the interests of protecting people.

Parables About Hypocrisy – Luke 6: 37-49

The 'Sermon on the Plain' finishes with a series of Parables around the theme of HYPOCRISY. Hypocrisy is 'saying one thing but doing the opposite' and someone whose words do not match their behaviour is a HYPOCRITE. *Hypocrisy/hypocrite* occurs 20 times in the Synoptic Gospels (but never in **John's Gospel**, oddly) and is a major theme of Jesus' ethical teaching.

The word comes from the Greek hupokrisis *which means 'to play a part', like an actor in the theatre. Hypocrites are like actors: they are pretending to be better than they really are.*

Warning about judging others – Luke 6: 37-42

Jesus warns about 'judging' other people, specifically condemning them for their faults. He advises people that God will judge them the y they judge others: if you are merciful and forgiving, you will receive mercy and forgiveness from God, but if you are hard-hearted and punish others for their sins, God will punish you for yours.

> *For with the measure you use, it will be measured to you* – **Luke 6: 38**

Frank J. Matera explains the psychology behind this advice:

> *Human judgement is flawed because it cannot fully understand the heart and motives of the other. Moreover, those who judge others rarely understand their own motives and faults* – **Frank J. Matera**

Jesus illustrates this with two short Parables:

- **The Blind Leading the Blind (Luke 6: 39-40):** This is the image of one blind person pretending to be sighted so he can guide another blind person – but of course *they both fall into a pit.* The hypocrisy here is that the so-called guide is pretending to be wiser and more insightful than he really is.
- **The Log in the Eye (Luke 6: 41-42):** This is the image of someone pointing out that their friend has a *speck of sawdust* in their eye (representing any minor fault or mistake), while the whole time they have a *plank* in their own eye. The hypocrisy here is that the critic is even more guilty than the person they are criticizing.

Both of these short Parables are intended to be funny as well as wise. It's not just John's Gospel that tells jokes!

Jesus clearly addresses this to his Disciples (using the term *brother* for each other). There's also a difference between JUDGEMENTALISM (hypocritically judging others when you have no right to) and MORAL CORRECTION (rightly pointing out when someone has made a mistake or is behaving badly).

The Tree & its Fruit – Luke 6: 43-45

This short Parable uses the symbolism of different types of fruit trees for different types of people. *Figs* and *grapes* are very desirable fruits, but you don't go looking for them in *thornbushes* and *briers*.

The sweet fruits are good actions; the thornbushes and briers are sinful people who don't produce good actions (but like to talk as if they do).

This could be summed up as 'actions speak louder than words' – never mind what people *say* they believe in and care about, what matters is what they *do*.

Hypocrites talk as if they are deeply moral people, but they don't act in a moral way.

This links to other agricultural symbols that Jesus uses:

Tasty figs on a fig tree

- **The Fig Tree:** In the Old Testament, the Fig Tree symbolises the Jewish nation itself. Jesus accuses the Jewish priests of being spiritually dead: this is the lack of fruit on the Fig Tree of Israel. In **Mark 11: 12-14**, Jesus curses a fig tree that has no fruit on it; since he does this immediately before **cleansing the Temple** we can be confident the fig tree represents the Jewish religion of the 1st century

- **The True Vine:** In **John's Gospel**, Jesus states **"I am the True Vine"** and his Disciples are the *branches that bear fruit* but the Jewish religion is represented by the fruitless branches that God cuts away.

- **The Parable of the Sower:** This Parable also the idea of a harvest growing from a seed that lands in good soil, representing people who listen to Jesus' teachings and genuinely act on them, contrasted with the other seeds that land on bad soil and produce no harvest.

When Jesus is about to be arrested, he compares the suffering ahead of him to drinking a cup of wine (e.g. **Luke 22: 42**) – wine is made from grapes, so suffering is the fruit of the vine too.

Later on, when the early Christians faced persecution and some turned away from their faith, the symbol of the trees bearing fruit took on another meaning: the good trees produce the fruit of suffering and martyrdom whereas the bad trees do not.

Wise & Foolish Builders – Luke 6: 46-49

Jesus compares his teaching to rock foundations for a house: anything built on them will last and survive the *torrent* (flood) that is coming. In contrast, trying to live your life ignoring these foundations is like building a house without solid foundations: when the *torrent* comes, the house is destroyed.

But what is the *house* and what is the coming *torrent*?

The house could be an individual's life. Jesus uses this sort of symbolism in the Parable of the demon **Beelzebub** invading a strong man's house (**Luke 11: 14-28**); the *torrent* would represent setbacks in life, temptations and persecutions, perhaps ultimately death itself. The *wise builder* is a Disciple who will survive all these things and receive Eternal Life because she followed Jesus' teachings. The *foolish builder* is someone following another code in life (such as a pagan religion or a philosophy like Stoicism or atheism). They are overwhelmed by the problems in life and, ultimately, they do not receive Eternal Life.

The house on strong foundations could be the Church and the house without foundations is the Jewish religion. The *torrent* is the events of history still to come: the Jewish War of 67-73 CE, the persecutions by the Romans, and so on through the centuries. Christianity has endured, but the **Pharisees, Sadducees, Essenes** and **Zealots** have all vanished.

The Parable could have an eschatological meaning, with the *torrent* representing the Apocalypse. Jesus uses similar imagery of some surviving the arrival of the Kingdom of God and others being swept away, for example the **Coming of the Kingdom** in **Luke 17: 20-37**.

The link to hypocrisy is in the opening line: people address Jesus as '*Lord*' but they do not follow his teachings. In other words, they pretend to be Christians, but they do not produce the fruits of good actions.

> **1st century Judaism:** The Jewish religion of the 1st century was based around many forms of external behaviour: making sacrifices, washing, wearing certain clothes, avoiding certain foods, keeping the Sabbath regulations. This made it easy to judge, in a superficial way, who was a 'good Jew' and who was not. Jesus criticises this sort of religiosity as HYPOCRITICAL: a person can keep all the outwards requirements of the Jewish religion and still harbour evil thoughts, never going out of their way to do good for other people.
>
> There is scholarly debate about whether this sort of assessment of ancient Judaism is fair. **Form** and **Redaction Criticism** argue it is really an attitude of the early Christians towards the Jews who rejected them, not an attitude that Jesus would have had towards his fellow-Jews.
>
> However, Jesus does seem to reinterpret Jewish morality in a much more personal way, focusing on loving motives and positive altruism. In this way, his teachings are a development on traditional Jewish ethics.

Christian codes of living: The challenge to live authentically, without hypocrisy, is not easy. Christianity became the official religion of the Roman Empire in the 4th century, introducing a social pressure to **appear** to be a pious Christian by attending church, praying, etc.

Reformers rebelled against this sort of hypocritical Christianity, particularly the existentialist philosophers like **Søren Kierkegaard** (who criticised the respectable Christianity of 19th century Denmark). **Existentialism** values authenticity above all else and this is **Rudolf Bultmann**'s reason for de-mythologizing Christianity to make its existentialist message more accessible to modern people.

Equality today: The warnings abut judging others contribute to the popularity of egalitarian practices. Discrimination usually begins by judging other groups harshly (prejudice), then acting on those judgments to treat members of these groups unfairly.

Augustine's motto of '*love the sinner, hate the sin*' enables some Christians to make harsh judgements about BEHAVIOUR that goes against their Christian principles (such as abortion, euthanasia or same-sex marriage) while still loving and not judging the PERSON who does things.

However, not everyone feels this is a fair distinction to make. For example, saying to someone who is obese '*I love you, it's your fatness I hate*' would be very hurtful: homosexuals similarly feel that their sexuality is part of their identity, not something that can be separated from them and treated as sinful while the non-sexual part of them is 'loved' in some abstract way.

Pluralism today: In the same way, religious liberty and religious tolerance are based on not judging members of other churches or religions. However, the warning about *false prophets* is exclusivist, suggesting that one version of Christianity is the true one and other churches and religions are condemned as false.

However, there is a tension here: Christians are commanded not to judge, but they are also commanded to preach the Gospel. Preaching the Gospel involves criticising immoral or blasphemous behaviour and trying to convert atheists and members of other religions, which goes against the idea of religious pluralism. Christians who **don't** try to convert friends, neighbours and work colleagues can be criticized for HYPOCRISY: they claim to follow Jesus but, like the *foolish builders*, they *don't do what he says*.

Evaluating the Sermon on the Plain

The 'Sermon on the Plain' is less influential than its longer equivalent, the 'Sermon on the Mount' in **Matthew's Gospel**. Matthew's Sermon has specific teachings on matters like murder, adultery, divorce, swearing oaths, prayer, fasting and donating to the poor.

The 'Sermon on the Plain' is less specific, offering broad principles instead. Nevertheless, it's more succinct and contains key Christian teachings such as the Golden Rule and commandments about loving your enemies and not judging others.

The Sermon sets out a clear picture of the Christian ethical life, but perhaps an impractical one. If people who are poor or hungry are 'blessed', is it a priority to reduce poverty and hunger in the world? Just how rich do you have to be to count as one of the well-fed and wealthy? Do these blessings and 'woes' apply only to individuals or to entire societies? For example, the Central African Republic, the Democratic Republic of the Congo and Burundi are the poorest nations on earth. Does that mean they are 'blessed'? Qatar, Luxembourg and Singapore are the richest: should they feel guilty about that?

Similarly, the instruction to love your enemy and not to judge becomes impractical if applied in society: should criminals be set free because, at the end of the day, only God can judge them? Should managers not fire employees who break the rules or underperform because that involves condemning someone? The Sermon is usually understood to apply to people's private lives rather than political or business decisions. However, this can lead to inconsistencies where someone is endlessly forgiving of friends and family, but harsh in their job as a magistrate or boss.

However, **Frank J. Matera** rejects the idea that the Sermon is impractical or intended to be for only the most dedicated followers:

> *Jesus expects those who hear the sermon to do what he teaches. He is not presenting an impossible ideal. Nor does he intend his sermon for the chosen few* – **Frank J. Matera**

Matera argues that critics who find Jesus' ideals too impractical make the mistake of imagining he is speaking to INDIVIDUALS. People who try to put the sermon into practice as individuals *"will always be frustrated."* Matera believes the Sermon is preached to *"a community of like-minded disciples"* – in other words, a church.

> *Those who live in a community in light of the in-breaking kingdom of God, however, will find the strength to live the ethic Jesus presents here* – **Frank J. Matera**

We are to imagine a Christian community trying to live by this ethic and taking part in the **Kingdom of God** on Earth by doing this. Viewed this way, Jesus' sermon seems more attainable and very attractive.

Does the Sermon on the Plain provide a basis for how to live in the modern world?

YES	NO
The Golden Rule as stated by Jesus has never been improved on as a basis for morality: *do as you would be done by* makes everyone ask themselves how **they** would wish to be treated, then treat others that way. The world would be a more equal and tolerant place if people practiced love towards their enemies and refrained from judging others.	The Sermon only provides broad principles but these collapse as soon as you try to apply them to specific situations. The Golden Rule doesn't answer questions like abortion or euthanasia because we can't imagine how we would like to be treated if we were a foetus or terminally ill. Human rights provide a stronger basis for securing equality and tolerance in society.
The Sermon can be applied to specific situations if further principles are used alongside it, such as **Augustine**'s *love the sinner but hate the sin* or **Aquinas**' Natural Moral Law. The Sermon provides the vision of the Christian moral life: loving, forgiving, non-judgmental and expressing itself in altruism towards other people. The practical details can be worked out separately.	The Sermon describes a moral outlook that is **eschatological** – rooted in the expectation that the world is about to end or in the Afterlife. Modern morality needs to be humanistic, rooted in this world's problems and solutions. The self-denying qualities Jesus recommends are not practical in a secular society where people have to be bosses, magistrates, policemen, soldiers and politicians.

Parable of the Good Samaritan (Luke 10)

These three Parables make up the final extract #10 of the Edexcel Anthology for this course

This is probably Jesus' most famous Parable; being a 'good samaritan' is a popular phrase for being a helpful stranger. The Parable occurs only in Luke's Gospel and beautifully illustrates Luke's major themes of compassion and the ethical use of money.

But before we start...

Who are the Samaritans?

The Samaritans are the inhabitants of **Samaria**, a highland region nestled between the rugged hills and deserts of Judea in the south and the fertile valleys of Galilee in the north.

Centuries earlier, Samaria had been the heartland of the Jewish kingdom of Israel which was conquered by the Assyrian Empire in 720 BCE. The ten northern tribes of the Israelites were taken away as slaves and disappear from history, leaving only the Kingdom of Judah in the south to carry on the Israelite lineage and the Jewish religion. The Assyrians resettled pagan tribes in Samaria and their descendants are the current Samaritans.

Or that's how they tell it in Judea. The Samaritans themselves claim to be the surviving descendants of the ancient Israelites. They worship God on Mount Gerizim in Samaria rather than in Jerusalem, they have their own version of the Torah and they claim that **their** religion is the original religion of the Israelites from before the Babylonian Exile. They too wait for a messiah that they call the 'Taheb' (meaning 'Restorer').

The Samaritans still exist today in the State of Israel, but they number about 700 and this is shrinking because they only marry within their own group and do not encourage anyone to convert to their religion.

Needless to say, two groups who both claim to be the original worshippers of the same God are **not** going to get along.

Jewish and Samaritan religious leaders taught that it was wrong to have any contact with the other group. Jews were not supposed to enter Samaritan territory or even speak to Samaritans. The historian **Flavius Josephus** reports battles between Jews and Samaritans in the 1st century and the Romans used Samaritan soldiers to keep order in Judea – so the Roman soldiers who mocked and executed Jesus were probably Samaritans, not Italians from Rome.

Jesus & the Samaritans: Jesus seems to have an unusual amount of contact with the Samaritans and is willing to speak with them. **Luke 9: 51-53** describes Jesus trying to stay overnight at a Samaritan village but being turned away because he is a Jew; however **Luke 17: 11-19** describes Jesus healing 10 lepers but the only one who thanks him is a Samaritan, whom Jesus praises. **John 4: 4-42** describes Jesus stopping in at a well in Samaria, speaking to a Samaritan woman and converting her family. Jesus seems to accept her claim that her people are Israelites too. **Acts 8: 1-25** describes Phillip, Peter and John converting many Samaritans to Christianity.

Raymond E. Brown proposes that the Johannine Community that composed **John's Gospel** contained a mixture of Jewish Christians and Samaritan Christians and that some of John's distinctive ideas and traditions might have come from this Samaritan influence.

The Context of the Parable

Jesus is being questioned by *an expert in the Law* (presumably a **Pharisee**) who wants to know how to achieve **Eternal Life**. Jesus bounces the question back at him and the Pharisee answers:

> "'Love the Lord your God with all your heart and with all your soul and with all your strength and with all your mind; and, 'Love your neighbour as yourself.'"

This is Jesus' own teaching: it is the 'Great Commandment' that Jesus explains in **Mark 12: 28-31** and **Matthew 22: 35-40**. In both cases, Jesus explains the Commandment to a *scribe* (in Mark) or a *lawyer* (in Matthew), so this *expert in the law* might be intended to be the same person that Jesus has previously taught.

This time, the Pharisee has another question: *"Who is my neighbour?"* Jesus, perhaps sensing the Pharisee is being deliberately awkward, answers with the Parable.

The Parable

> "A man was going down from Jerusalem to Jericho, when he was attacked by robbers. They stripped him of his clothes, beat him and went away, leaving him half dead. 31 A priest happened to be going down the same road, and when he saw the man, he passed by on the other side. 32 So too, a Levite, when he came to the place and saw him, passed by on the other side. 33 But a Samaritan, as he travelled, came where the man was; and when he saw him, he took pity on him. 34 He went to him and bandaged his wounds, pouring on oil and wine. Then he put the man on his own donkey, brought him to an inn and took care of him. 35 The next day he took out two denarii and gave them to the innkeeper. 'Look after him,' he said, 'and when I return, I will reimburse you for any extra expense you may have.'

Jerusalem is up in the mountains (2500 feet above sea level) but the ancient city of Jericho to the north is 825 feet *below* sea level which is why the man *goes down* to Jericho.

Although the route connecting the cities is only about 18 miles, it is steep and difficult to travel, dropping from cold mountains into dry desert. Worse than that, the road was known as 'the Way of Blood' because of the number of murders that took place on it, due to gangs of bandits that could lie in wait among the cliffs and crags.

This traveller falls victim to such a gang and is left for dead. Two travellers pass him as he lies near death but refuse to help:

- A **priest** from the Temple in Jerusalem
- A **Levite** (a clan of Jewish monks who assisted with priestly sacrifices)

Although these two men are supposed to embody all the values of the Jewish religion, they show no compassion. This might be because of the danger (the robbers might return) but also because the man appears dead and touching a corpse would make a priest or Levite ritually unclean and they would be unable to perform their duties (so this is putting religious rules ahead of moral duties).

The third traveller *does* help – and in fact goes out of his way to look after the victim, treating him himself then bringing him to an inn and paying the bills to have the man looked after. This compassionate stranger is a Samaritan, someone no sensible Jew would talk to or expect to get help from.

The Conclusion

Jesus asks, which one of the three was the victim's neighbour? The Pharisee, clearly unwilling even to *name* the Samaritan, answers: *"the one who had mercy on him."*

Jesus tells the Pharisee to go and be more like the Samaritan in future!

Interpreting the Parable

The Parable puts Jesus' teachings about *love your enemy* (from the **Sermon on the Plain**) into action: Samaritans and Jews are supposed to be enemies, yet the Samaritan shows compassion for his enemy and goes to personal expense to see that his enemy is cared for.

The moral is that we should treat all our enemies this way. In answer to the Pharisee's question *"Who is my neighbour?"* the answer is: *Anyone in need of help or compassion!*

The Pharisee's prejudices have also been challenged: he thought he understood the 'Great Commandment' but Jesus has used this Parable to reveal what *loving your neighbour* really means – and it's something the Pharisee is uncomfortable with.

The Parable also illustrates the **Kingdom of God** coming about in surprising ways, which is an important theme in Luke's Gospel.

Christian scholars like **Irenaeus** and **Origen** interpreted the Parable **allegorically**:

- The road from Jerusalem to Jericho is the descent from Paradise/the Garden of Eden to the Fallen world of sin (i.e. all human history)
- The traveller is the soul of every human being
- The robbers are the forces of evil and the traveller's wounds are sins
- The Priest and Levite represent the **Law**, which is powerless to help people
- The Samaritan is Christ who comes as a **Saviour**
- The donkey that bears the wounded man is Christ's body, which takes on the burden of human sins by his atoning death on the Cross
- The inn represents the Church, which does Christ's work on earth
- The Samaritan promises to return, which is *Parousia* (the 'Second Coming')

This allegorical interpretation is also a good illustration of the concept of **salvation-history** in Luke's Gospel *(c.f. **Topic 5.1 Kingdom of God in Luke**)*.

1st century Judaism: Jesus' 'Great Commandment' is based on Jewish Scriptures. **Deuteronomy 6:5** commands Jews to *"love the Lord your God with all your heart and with all your soul and with all your might"* and this forms part of the *Shema*, a daily prayer offered by Jews to this day. **Leviticus 19: 18** contains the instruction to *"love your neighbour as yourself."*

What Jesus does is place these two together, making the authentic love of God ***the same thing*** as the love of your neighbour, so that you can't properly do one without the other. Jesus also UNIVERSALISES the instruction to *love your neighbour*, by making *neighbour* mean ***anyone*** rather than just fellow-Jews.

Christian codes of living: This Parable profoundly influenced Christian ethics, leading to the founding of hospitals, charities and other institutions to care for the needy.

In 1953, the **Rev. Chad Varah** founded a new charity, staffed by volunteers, who would support depressed and suicidal people through a free telephone helpline (tel: 116 123). He named this organisation 'the Samaritans' to show his debt to Jesus' Parable and ethic of compassion. Varah was motivated to do this by the funeral of a 14 year old girl who had committed suicide, fearing she had contracted a STD; in fact, she had started menstruating but had no one she could talk to about her problems.

The Parable also illustrates the ethical use of money to help others (and as an alternative to the belief that Christians must live in 'holy poverty').

The UK Prime Minister **Margaret Thatcher** used the Parable to illustrate this positive view of wealth in 1980 when she told a TV interview:

*No one would remember the Good Samaritan if he'd only had good intentions; he had money as well – **Margaret Thatcher***

However, critics argue that this distorts the message of the Parable, since the only person in the story motivated solely by money is the innkeeper (who must be paid to care for the wounded man), but the point of the Parable is that we should be like the Samaritan rather than the Innkeeper.

Equality today: The Parable offers a powerful message of equality, showing that differences of race, nationality and culture are meaningless compared to the duty to show compassion to fellow human beings.

Matt Broomfield, writing in *The Spectator* (2017) argues that we should all give unconditionally to street beggars, even if we suspect they're drug addicts:

*If your money funds the final hit, accept that the person would rather be dead. If your act of kindness makes him wake up the next morning and decide to change his life, that's nice but not your business either – **Matt Broomfield***

Not many Christians would be comfortable with the thought of an addict overdosing using their donation, but Broomfield's argument that giving to the needy should be unconditional and direct, without making moral judgments about why they are in that position, is very close to the spirit of the Parable and to the **Sermon on the Plain**.

Pluralism today: The clearest message of the Parable is one of religious pluralism: the Jews and the Samaritans worship the *same God* who wants them to love each other as he loves them. Religious distinctions (like the religious rituals of the priest and the Levite) are distractions from the true duty to love God through loving your neighbour.

This interpretation has not been emphasized over the centuries (and the allegorical interpretation of the Samaritan as Christ perhaps distracts from this meaning). Christians were inspired by the Parable to build hospitals and orphanages, but not to reconcile with Jews (whom they accused of 'deicide' – the murder of God).

However, in the 1960s the **Second Vatican Council** changed the Catholic Church's position on many things, including rejecting the concept of Jewish 'deicide' and focusing on the *'shared patrimony'* (inheritance) of Christians and Jews.

Parables of the Lost (Luke 15)

These three Parables emphasize the qualities of compassion and God's mercy that are particularly important in **Luke's Gospel**.

The context is important. The **Pharisees** are *muttering* that Jesus associates with *sinners* and *eats with them*. The *sinners* are publicans (like the tax collector **Matthew/Levi** who becomes one of Jesus' Disciples and **Zacchaeus** who repented after Jesus dined with him). These people are sinners because they collaborate with the **Roman occupation** and swindle their fellow Jews. However, Jesus associates with other *sinners* too:

- **Prostitutes**, like the woman who anoints Jesus' feet (**Luke 7: 36-50**) and also (arguably the same person) the woman caught in adultery (**John 8: 1-11**)
- The **diseased**, like the lepers (**Luke 17: 11-19**} or the man who was blind from birth (**John 9: 1-3**), whose illness was regarded by 1st century Jews (but not by Jesus) as a punishment for sin
- **Samaritans**, like the Samaritan woman at the well (**John 4: 27** – even Jesus' Disciples are surprised by this)

The criticism of Jesus is not just that he associates with these people without judging them, but also that he makes himself ritually unclean (according to 1st century Jewish purity laws) by coming into contact with them.

The Lost Sheep

This is Jesus' immediate reply to the criticism that he associates with *sinners*:

> [4] "Suppose one of you has a hundred sheep and loses one of them. Doesn't he leave the ninety-nine in the open country and go after the lost sheep until he finds it? [5] And when he finds it, he joyfully puts it on his shoulders [6] and goes home. Then he calls his friends and neighbours together and says, 'Rejoice with me; I have found my lost sheep.' [7] I tell you that in the same way there will be more rejoicing in heaven over one sinner who repents than over ninety-nine righteous persons who do not need to repent.

Jesus' point is simple: his mission is to people who are 'lost' in sin, not to people who are already *righteous*. This links to Jesus' statement **"I Am the Good Shepherd"** (*c.f.* **Topic 2.2 Titles of Jesus**).

There is also the image here of the celebratory banquet, which Jesus uses to represent the **Kingdom of God** (*c.f.* Topic 5.1 **Kingdom of God in Luke**). The *sinners*, who know that they are sinners, have the opportunity to repent and enter the Kingdom of God; the Pharisees, who mistakenly believe themselves to be *righteous*, will not repent and will be excluded.

The Lost Coin

Jesus moves on to a more comedic response that makes a similar point:

> 8 "Or suppose a woman has ten silver coins and loses one. Doesn't she light a lamp, sweep the house and search carefully until she finds it? 9 And when she finds it, she calls her friends and neighbours together and says, 'Rejoice with me; I have found my lost coin.' 10 In the same way, I tell you, there is rejoicing in the presence of the angels of God over one sinner who repents."

Here, the woman searching for her coin represents God, searching for the lost souls. This represents the activity of God throughout human history, sending his prophets and ultimately sending Jesus himself (which may be the symbolism of the woman *lighting a lamp* – **John's Prologue** describes Jesus as the *Light that shines in the Darkness*).

As with the previous Parable (p71), there is celebration when the lost soul is found.

However, this Parable is more surprising, since God is depicted as a woman. More than that, the image of a Jewish woman obsessively turning the house upside down in the middle of the night over a single misplaced coin plays into a lot of comedy stereotypes about Jewish mothers.

> *Is Jesus making his audience laugh here with distinctively Jewish humour? It's interesting that the NARRATOR of John's Gospel is often witty, but in the Synoptic Gospels Jesus **himself** is frequently witty. Although the Gospels present Jesus as crying, they never state that he laughed – but I think he certainly made his audiences laugh!*

The Lost Son

This Parable is often called the 'Prodigal Son' ('prodigal' meaning 'careless with money'). It is second only to the **Parable of the Good Samaritan** (p66) in terms of its influence in Christian thought. It represents a complete illustration of Jesus' teaching about lost souls and the **Kingdom of God**.

The story concerns a farmer with two sons. Rather than wait for his inheritance, the younger son wants the money up-front, so his father *divides his estate* (presumably selling off land to raise money for the younger son). The younger son shows no gratitude or respect:

> 13 "Not long after that, the younger son got together all he had, set off for a distant country and there squandered his wealth in wild living. 14 After he had spent everything, there was a severe famine in that whole country, and he began to be in need. 15 So he went and hired himself out to a citizen of that country, who sent him to his fields to feed pigs. 16 He longed to fill his stomach with the pods that the pigs were eating, but no one gave him anything.

The younger son is 'prodigal' by spending everything in *wild living* (with *prostitutes*, we later learn). It's worth noticing that the prodigal son is living among Gentiles: he has gone to *a distant country* and ends up *feeding pigs* (no Jewish farmer would keep pigs).

The prodigal son is thoroughly degraded. He is cut off from his people and his religion. He lives among Gentiles and is ritually polluted by working with pigs. In other words, his position is exactly the same as the publicans and other *sinners* that Jesus associates with.

The prodigal son has hit rock bottom but *no one gave him anything* – he's not even allowed to eat pig swill! This represents the way publicans and other *sinners* are ostracised by respectable Jews. Of course, 1st century publicans weren't living in poverty: working for the Romans made them well-off. However, they were spiritually poor, because they were cut off from worshiping God – and the prostitutes and lepers were probably poor in wealth as well.

The prodigal son decides to go back to his father. He's too ashamed to ask for forgiveness. He intends to ask for a job as a labourer on his father's farm. He feels he has lost forever the right to be called his father's son. This represents his sincere repentance.

> "But while he was still a long way off, his father saw him and was filled with compassion for him; he ran to his son, threw his arms around him and kissed him.
>
> 21 "The son said to him, 'Father, I have sinned against heaven and against you. I am no longer worthy to be called your son.'
>
> 22 "But the father said to his servants, 'Quick! Bring the best robe and put it on him. Put a ring on his finger and sandals on his feet. 23 Bring the fattened calf and kill it. Let's have a feast and celebrate. 24 For this son of mine was dead and is alive again; he was lost and is found.' So they began to celebrate.

This passage makes the same point as the previous Parables. The father is God and the prodigal son is a soul lost to sin. When the sinner repents, God rejoices and there is a celebration and a banquet. The sinner's sins are utterly forgiven: *he was lost and is found*.

However, the Parable does not end here. Jesus explores the implications of repentance in greater depth by considering the **other** son who stayed at home and did his duty. This son is resentful towards his younger brother and the celebration over his return:

> 28 "The older brother became angry and refused to go in. So his father went out and pleaded with him. 29 But he answered his father, 'Look! All these years I've been slaving for you and never disobeyed your orders. Yet you never gave me even a young goat so I could celebrate with my friends. 30 But when this son of yours who has squandered your property with prostitutes comes home, you kill the fattened calf for him!'
>
> 31 "'My son,' the father said, 'you are always with me, and everything I have is yours. 32 But we had to celebrate and be glad, because this brother of yours was dead and is alive again; he was lost and is found.'"

The older son represents the Pharisees who keep the Jewish **Law**. There is something self-righteous about him: he is proud but he works for his father out of hope of reward rather than love. He sees himself as a *slave* rather than a son.

Many critics detect insolence in the older son's words. He says "*Look...*" to his father rather than addressing him as "*Father*" – and of course Jesus teaches his Disciples to address God as their *Father in Heaven*.

It's significant that the older son cannot name his own brother, calling him "*this son of yours*" (rather like the Pharisee in the **Parable of the Good Samaritan** who cannot bring himself to name the Samaritan). By contrast, Jesus encourages his Disciples to call each other 'brother'.

The father's response, like God's, is painstaking and compassionate. He does not get angry. He assures the brother that *you are always with me and everything I have is yours*. There is a gentle irony in the way he refers to the prodigal son as *this brother of yours* – echoing the older son's hard-hearted words to bring him to his senses and reminding readers that *all* unfortunate people who suffer hardship and ostracism are really their *brothers*.

The Parable ends there, unresolved. Will the older son soften his heart and be reconciled with his brother? Or will he stay out in the fields, angry and self-righteous, while the party goes on back at the house? This is a question the Pharisees must answer for themselves: will they enter the **Kingdom of Heaven** alongside the repentant publicans, prostitutes, lepers and Samaritans – or be left out like the ungrateful guests in the **Parable of the Great Banquet** (*c.f.* **Topic 5.1**)?

> *It's odd that this Parable is known as the **Parable of the Prodigal Son**, when really it's not about him at all. The truly 'lost son' is not the prodigal but the one who stayed behind but never learned to love his father. Really, it should be the 'Parable of the Dutiful Son'.*

1st century Judaism: Many of the details here must be contextualised: the ritual pollution from working with pigs or socialising with Gentiles. This Parable emphasises the hard-hearted nature of **Phariseeism** (which calculates how much God owes us for our good deeds rather than loving God in a humble spirit). Scholars are divided over whether this is a fair representation of what Pharisees were actually like, but it's certainly what later Christians *thought* they were like, so **Form Critics** would treat this story is a *pericope* expressing the attitudes of 1st century Christians (who saw themselves as the prodigal son and the Jews as the hard-hearted older brother).

Christian codes of living: The key theme for Christians is REPENTANCE and the importance of second chances. Christians are supposed to be like the father (delighted when somebody repents) rather than the older son (still angry about the sins they have repented). However, Christians did not find this code easy to live by.

For one thing, sexual misconduct troubled early Christians and led to lapsed members being expelled from churches and not forgiven. It is interesting that the prodigal son's sins included fornication, because this was rarely tolerated by the early Church.

Another problem was what to do with former-Christians who denied their faith during persecutions then wanted to return to the Church when the persecutions ended.

The Church soon developed the institution of confessing sins and asking for forgiveness – and divided sins into VENAL sins (which could be forgiven by your fellow-Christians) and MORTAL sins (which could only be forgiven by God).

The Catholic Church continues the practice of EXCOMMUNICATING members who commit mortal sins. Excommunicants cannot receive the Church's sacraments (including the Eucharist). Throughout history, excommunication was used to control people (including kings and queens) with the threat of damnation after death.

Equality today: The Parable's message of repentance and forgiveness is still important for individuals but also takes on a social dimension in the 21st century. There are historic crimes (such as slavery, colonialism, genocide and environmental damage) of which entire societies are responsible. This is COLLECTIVE GUILT and the need for NATIONAL REPENTANCE.

One country that has taken on this message is post-war Germany, which has engaged in national repentance over the Holocaust and other Nazi atrocities. Similarly, in 2007, the UK Government apologized for its historic role in the slave trade.

However, it's one thing to apologise but another to REPENT. People in Western societies continue to benefit from the crimes committed by their ancestors (for example, by the wealth taken from former-colonies or generated by slave labour). Some argue that equality demands that victims are COMPENSATED for historic crimes. For example, Germany makes reparations to the State of Israel to compensate Holocaust survivors and the families of victims. However, Western nations have not offered reparation to countries in Africa or Asia for mistreatment in the past, despite huge inequalities in wealth that continue to exist.

Pluralism today: Many religious divisions are based on historic grievances. Christian antisemitism has occurred for centuries, but the Crusades that began in the 11th century CE created historic grievances between Christians and Muslims. The Reformation and the European Wars of Religion that followed in the 16th-17th centuries have left behind mistrust and bitterness between Catholics and Protestants that continue to this day in places like Northern Ireland. Such hostility makes religious tolerance difficult.

There have been moves towards greater religious tolerance. In 2000, the Catholic Church formally apologised for sins committed against Jews, heretics, Gypsies and native peoples. Many religious groups are in the position of the older son rather than his prodigal younger brother: it's hard for them to admit their role in historic evils because they see themselves as righteous and acting in accordance with divinely-inspired teachings. The words of the father are a reassurance from God to repent: *you are always with me and everything I have is yours.*

Parable of the Rich Man and Lazarus (Luke 16)

There has been a debate over the years about whether this story is a Parable at all or a description of actual events. **Luke's Gospel** does not introduce this as a Parable and it's unusual for Parables to give the main characters names (usually they are just 'a traveller', 'a man who had two sons' or 'a sower'). On the other hand, the story functions like a Parable. **I. Howard Marshall** argues it is a Middle Eastern (possibly Egyptian) folk tale, which Jesus has adapted by giving the characters new names:

> the background to the teaching is more probably found in non-biblical sources – **I. Howard Marshall**

> The 'Lazarus' in the story is not the same Lazarus who is raised from the dead in **John's Gospel**. The Rich Man is sometimes named 'Dives'. This is based on misreading the Latin text ('dives' just means 'wealthy') but Dives is as good a name as any so I'll use it in this analysis.

In context, Jesus has been telling Parables about money to the **Pharisees** "who loved money ... and were sneering at Jesus". Jesus warns them that they *cannot serve two masters*:

> You cannot serve both God and money – **Luke 16: 13**

The Parable follows on from this, illustrating Jesus' attitude to wealth and to the Pharisees.

The Parable

Dives is a rich man who lives in luxury; Lazarus is a beggar covered in sores who lives in the street. When the two men die, they go to different Afterlife destinations:

- Dives goes to *Hades*, a place of fiery suffering
- Lazarus goes to *Abraham's side*, in paradise where he is welcomed by Abraham, the founder of the Jewish race and religion

Dives begs Abraham for help: will he send Lazarus down to place a drop of water on Dives' tongue? Abraham declines, saying:

> 'Son, remember that in your lifetime you received your good things, while Lazarus received bad things, but now he is comforted here and you are in agony. [26] And besides all this, between us and you a great chasm has been set in place, so that those who want to go from here to you cannot, nor can anyone cross over from there to us.'

When Abraham says that Dives has already *received his good things*, this echoes Jesus' teaching in the **Sermon on the Plain**, that the rich have *already received their comfort* but the poor will *receive the Kingdom of God*.

There is a debate among Christians about who Lazarus and Dives are supposed to be and where they end up.

- Some see Dives as a purely symbolic figure for 'wealthy people. Others think he represents the **Pharisees** (whom Jesus is addressing in context**). Johann Sepp** (1864) suggests that the description of Dives wearing the *purple robes* and *living in luxury* suggests a **Sadducee** rather than a Pharisee.
- Lazarus represents all poor people. His *sores* suggest he is a leper and 1st century Judaism regarded leprosy as a punishment for sin. This links to the **Parables of the Lost** (p71) because Lazarus would be one of the *sinners* that Jesus associates with and this Parable also rejects the belief that there is a link between sickness and sin.

The description of the Afterlife also poses problems for Christian interpretation:

- Lazarus is in some sort of paradise, but is this supposed to be Heaven? Since Jesus has not yet died his atoning death, how could Lazarus go to Heaven? Lazarus seems to be in the 'Bosom of Abraham', a belief of the **Pharisees** that the righteous dead would go to a comfortable Afterlife to wait for Judgement Day.
- Dives is in a state of torment. Conservative Christians take this Parable as evidence of the literal existence of Hell as a place of eternal punishment. Others point out that the term *Hades* is a Greek translation of the Hebrew *SHEOL* which just means "the grave"; for them, Dives is frightened of his ***future*** suffering on Judgement Day.

Many Christian scholars, such as **Martin Luther** (1483-1546), regard the afterlife details in this Parable as purely **symbolic**: what matters is just that Lazarus and Dives have SWAPPED ROLES, just as Jesus warned in his Beatitudes and Woes during the **Sermon on the Plain** (p53).

Dives' servants tell Lazarus to leave

It's interesting that the Afterlife in this Parable doesn't match with Jesus' own eschatological predictions. Rather than 'the Bosom of Abraham', Jesus preaches about the Kingdom of God as something happening on Earth; the people who enter the Kingdom are repentant sinners but those who are shut out have rejected the Kingdom: the Kingdom hasn't rejected them.

One interpretation is that, in this Parable, Jesus is describing the Pharisees' ***own*** religious beliefs about the Afterlife rather than his own teachings. His point is that the Pharisees stand to be condemned even in terms of their ***own*** beliefs because they do not *love their neighbours*.

The punch-line of the Parable is probably more important than the details about the Afterlife:

'Then I beg you, father, send Lazarus to my family, [28] for I have five brothers. Let him warn them, so that they will not also come to this place of torment.'

[29] "Abraham replied, 'They have Moses and the Prophets; let them listen to them.'

[30] "'No, father Abraham,' he said, 'but if someone from the dead goes to them, they will repent.'

[31] "He said to him, 'If they do not listen to Moses and the Prophets, they will not be convinced even if someone rises from the dead.'"

The Parable shows that God's demand for fairness and charity is well-attested in *Moses and the Prophets* (i.e. the Written Torah and the Oral Law of the Pharisees), but that the Pharisees themselves ignore what the **Law** says.

The prediction that people who ignore the Scriptures won't be convinced by a man rising from the dead looks ahead to Jesus' **Resurrection**. The Pharisees will continue to dismiss Jesus' teachings even after the Resurrection. Furthermore, in Luke's account of the Resurrection, people only *believe* after Jesus has *opened their minds* to the true meaning of the Scriptures, which all refer to his atoning sacrifice (*c.f.* **Topic 5.3**).

1st century Judaism: This Parable is strongly rooted in 1st century Jewish beliefs about the afterlife, specifically the **Pharisees'** beliefs. The ideas of the 'Bosom of Abraham' for the righteous dead, *SHEOL* (the Grave) for everyone else, and a Judgment Day when the dead are resurrected to be punished or rewarded: these are all Jewish beliefs from the time period. Similarly, the moral commandment to care for the poor and give your wealth to the needy is part of Judaism too. Jesus' critique is that these beliefs don't **motivate** people to live righteously.

Christian codes of living: This Parable reinforces Christian codes about the ethical use of wealth established in the **Sermon on the Plain** (p53) and illustrated in the **Parable of the Good Samaritan** (p66). It also reinforces Jesus' teaching that those who fail to show love and mercy in *this* life will not receive it from God in the Afterlife. However, Christians believe that their faith in Jesus' atoning death and Resurrection means that their sins will be forgiven if they fail to live up to the high standard God expects, so long as they sincerely tried.

Equality today: This Parable contains a powerful message concerning economic inequality. There is a tendency for Christians to over-emphasize sexual sins (such as the prodigal son and his prostitutes), but Jesus has far more to say about wealth than about sex. This Parable follows Jesus' warning that people *cannot serve two masters*: they must choose between God and money. A 2018 report by Oxfam shows the widening gap between the world's super-rich and everyone else, with 82% of wealth generated in the previous year going to the richest 1% of the population. The CEO of a big fashion retailer earns in 4 days what a Bangladeshi textile worker earns in an entire lifetime.

Pluralism today: If Jesus (or at any rate, Luke) really did adapt an Egyptian folk tale to represent Pharisee beliefs about the Afterlife (as **I. Howard Marshall** suggests) then this is a good example of religious pluralism, because it suggests that we can learn things from other religions too. For example, **David Burrell** (2014) argues Christians can learn from Islam, saying that *"the attraction of Islam can most often be traced to the palpable sense of community"* because Islam preserves a community spirit that Christianity has lost sight of. Jewish rabbi **Jonathan Sacks** (2002) argues for 'religious diversity', saying, *"no one civilization encompasses all the spiritual, ethical and artistic expressions of mankind"* and therefore all religions can learn from each other.

Do Luke's Parables provide a basis for how to live in the modern world?

YES	NO
The Parables show how the teachings from the Sermon on the Plain must be put into practice: the Good Samaritan illustrates loving your enemy, the Lost Son illustrates weeping turning to joy through repentance, the Rich Man & Lazarus shows the dangers of wealth and the blessings for the poor and hungry.	The Parables are too rooted in the world of the 1st century to guide people today: ethnic conflicts between Jews and Samaritans, Jewish purity laws, the politics of a Roman occupation and ancient mythologies about the afterlife. The 21st century is beset by complex problems of global inequality, environmental destruction and terrorism not covered by these.
The Parables have guided Christians for centuries, long after the original contexts were forgotten: it's not important who Samaritans were or what happens after we die, because the Parables illustrate loving *any* enemy and caring for *all* the poor in this life The Parable of the Lost Son invites religious people to examine their consciences even if they consider themselves to be good people and recognise every 'lost soul' as their brother, no matter what that person might have done in the past.	The Parables fly in the face of normal morality. While it's nice to 'love your enemy', you also have an obligation to look after your family and friends and protect your country; it's good to see bad people turn themselves around, but we should still reward good people for doing the right thing; giving to the needy is admirable, but people have also got a right to enjoy the wealth they have earned. No one seriously tries to act on the values in these Parables and society wouldn't work if they did.

Evaluating How We Should Live

If you also study **Unit 2 (Religion & Ethics)** then there is a lot of crossover with this topic, especially when it comes to answering the 'synoptic' essay question in Section C of either paper. With that in mind, let's look at two ethical theories from Religion & Ethics in the light of Luke's **Sermon on the Plain** (p53) and **Parables** (p66).

Natural Moral Law

Natural Moral Law (NML) was first expounded by **Aristotle** in the 4th century BCE and developed by **Thomas Aquinas** (1225-1274); it is the ethical system favoured by the Catholic Church today.

NML argues that there is a moral code that humans are naturally inclined towards. Aristotle starts by looking at the purpose (or '*telos*') of human life and concludes the natural human life is a rational life. Aristotle argues that, as rational creatures, we have an obligation to keep ourselves alive, to reproduce, and to live in an ordered society. Giving in to non-rational desires enslaves and degrades the individual, threatening our security and the security of our society.

Thomas Aquinas merged Aristotelian ideas with Christianity and he brings a strong religious dimension to this, saying that you cannot think about the purpose behind human life without considering the Afterlife and God: our ultimate *telos* is to enjoy communion with God forever.

The problem is that people choose "apparent goods" that make them happy in the short term (like drunkenness or fornication) rather than "actual goods" that secure them long term happiness (like sobriety or chastity). We can tell the difference between these apparent and actual goods by using "right reason".

For Aquinas, we do not invent morals, we discover them. God makes portions of his Eternal Law obvious to us through revelation, such as Jesus' teachings: this is the Divine Law. The Eternal Law can be worked out through observing nature, because God is the Creator of the universe: this is the Natural Law. So, for example, you don't need to be a Christian or read the Bible to work out that a life of drunkenness and casual sex will not, in the long run, make anyone happy or fulfilled. Humans then set up their own laws and social conventions, based on Natural Law, maybe mixed with bits of Divine Law: this is Positive Law, which is a human creation and therefore imperfect. For example, in the past Positive Law discriminated against women but over the centuries clearer thinking about Natural Law and interpreting Divine Law has led to greater equality for women.

Evaluating NML with reference to Jesus' teaching

On the face of it, NML seems a long way away from Jesus' ethical teaching. NML is all about laws that must be followed without exception (i.e. it is DEONTOLOGICAL). Jesus' ethics are all about the exceptions: love and forgive your enemy, don't judge other people, celebrate the repentant sinner more than the righteous person.

NML also contradicts the eschatological element of Jesus' teaching. It's a very this-worldly ethical system. It assumes that people want to work in jobs, raise a family, grow old and die peacefully. Jesus praises people who abandon their jobs and family to seek the Kingdom of God (**Luke 14: 26**) and warns about an Apocalypse that will end society as we know it; the earliest Christians did not expect to grow old, since Jesus predicted the *Parousia* ('Second Coming') before they died in **Luke 21: 32**.

This is why Aquinas' contribution to NML is important. Aquinas introduces the importance of the Afterlife and the idea of Divine Law (from the Bible) supplementing Natural Law (from common sense):

- Natural Law tells us that we don't want to have a huge gap between the rich and the poor because that leads to crime and revolution in society; Divine Law goes further with Jesus' teachings to give to the poor unselfishly
- Natural Law tells us to show some restraint in the way we punish enemies, otherwise society falls apart because of feuds and vendettas; Divine Law goes further with Jesus' teachings to forgive enemies unconditionally

In many ways, the strict rules of NML remain a 'bad fit' for Jesus' teachings, but Aquinas shows how Jesus' ethics supplement and complete an ethical code we can work out for ourselves.

Situation Ethics

Situation Ethics (SE) was first developed by **Joseph Fletcher** (1905-1991); it is an ethical system favoured by liberal Christians today.

Fletcher claimed he was inspired by a St Louis cab driver who said to him: *"Sometimes you've gotta put your principles to one side and do the right thing"*. Fletcher argues for the importance of the Christian idea of **agápē** (loving compassion) as the thing that makes our behaviour moral. We act out of love for others, trying to do the best for other people rather than ourselves.

SE states that decision-making should be based upon the circumstances of a particular situation, and not upon some fixed law or rule (LEGALISM). Fletcher founded his ethics upon **1 John 4: 8**: *"God is love."* The only absolute is Love. Love should be the motive behind every decision. As long as Love is your intention, the end justifies the means.

So a person who practises SE approaches ethical problems with some general moral principles rather than a complete set of ethical laws and is prepared to give up even those principles if doing so will lead to a greater good. Since *"circumstances alter cases,"* what in some times and places we call right is in other times and places wrong.

For example, lying is ordinarily not in the best interest of people and relationships, but is justifiable in certain situations (such as encouraging an ageing relative to believe that all is well in your troubled marriage).

Evaluating SE with reference to Jesus' teaching

On the face of it, SE seems a good fit with Jesus' ethics. The **Sermon on the Plain** (p53) boils down to a commandment to *love your neighbour* and this is illustrated in the **Parable of the Good Samaritan** (p66), where the Priest and the Levite's religious rules get in the way of their showing *agape*-love but the Samaritan breaks all the rules to show love to someone in need. The punishment of Dives in *Hades* can be interpreted as a condemnation of his failure to show love to Lazarus (because Fletcher says *"justice is love distributed"*).

However, conservative Christians have been reluctant to embrace SE. Jesus says he comes *not to abolish the Law but to fulfill it* (**Matthew 5: 17**) and SE sounds very much like it is abolishing the laws of morality. Jesus also warns against *false prophets* who will be popular but whose ethical teachings are like a *house built without a foundation*.

The conservative evangelical **William Barclay** (1971) opposes SE with this argument:

> *it is much easier to agree that extraordinary situations need extraordinary measures than to think that there are no laws for ordinary, everyday life* – **William Barclay**

Possibly, Fletcher only ever meant to argue that *extraordinary situations need extraordinary measures* and this might be all Jesus is saying too: the **Parable of the Good Samaritan** and the **Lost Son** both describe *extraordinary situations*. However, scholars like **I. Howard Marshall** do not accept SE as the best ethical interpretation of Jesus' teachings. Marshall recognises Fletcher's point that Biblical teachings have to be reinterpreted for the modern world but doesn't think we can just ignore 'difficult' teachings (e.g. about homosexuality being sinful).

Case Study: Westboro Baptist Church

The Westboro Baptist Church (WBC) is a church with less than 40 members, mostly the children of its founder, Fred Phelps (1929-2014). The congregation lives and worships together in a compound of houses in Topeka, Kansas. Many of the family are qualified lawyers and run a law firm that helps support the WBC's activities. Over the years, several family members have left the church to pursue normal American lives; these people are completely rejected by the WBC and can have no further contact with their parents, brothers and sisters.

In many ways, the WBC has beliefs that are quite typical of American evangelical churches. They believe humanity is living in the "End Times" and *Parousia* will happen soon, with Christ re-appearing on Earth to judge people for their sins.

However, in other ways the members of the WBC are extremists. They believe that they alone follow the true Christian faith so people who are atheists or follow other religions (e.g. Jews, Muslims, Hindus) will go to Hell and so will other Christians with different beliefs (e.g. Catholics, Anglicans, Methodists). Phelps argues that churches which preach about God's love are misleading people because he believes that the Bible makes it clear that God also hates; if you visit the WBC website, the first message you will see is the slogan 'God Hates You'.

However, the WBC attracts the most controversy for its stance on homosexuality. Most evangelical churches claim that homosexual sex is against the will of God, but they argue that although God hates the sin, he still loves the sinners. The WBC rejects this and claims America is under God's curse for tolerating homosexuality and all Americans who die in foreign wars or as victims of terrorism or disasters are being punished by God for America's sins. Members of the church picket outside military funerals with placards saying 'God Hates America'. This causes great distress to the families of the dead but the WBC believe they are doing God's will, arguing like this:

WBC picket in 2008 (photo: David Shankbone)

> *You think our job is to win souls to Christ? All we do, by getting in their face … is make what's already in their heart come out of their mouth* – **Shirley Phelps-Roper**

Making what's already in their hearts come out of their mouths links to Jesus' teaching about trees producing good and bad fruit. In other words, the WBC has no interest in making converts; they just want to make a clear distinction between people who ignore Biblical rules and people (like themselves) who condemn homosexuality, in preparation for Judgment Day.

Evaluating the WBC with reference to Jesus' teaching

The WBC's teachings and actions seem far-removed from Jesus' ethics. Jesus taught his Disciples to love their neighbours, forgive their enemies and not to judge, whereas the WBC deliberately causes distress to neighbours, is unforgiving of its opponents and behaves very judgmentally. Most ordinary Christians (including evangelicals) view Pastor Phelps is a *false preacher* who has led his congregation astray. However, the WBC's eschatological teaching about the End Times being imminent ***does*** link to Jesus' teaching and, from their view point, it is the ordinary Christians who have been led astray by *false preachers*.

Although the WBC's behaviour is completely out of line with Christian thought, it does illustrate a problem with applying Jesus' ethical teachings. The Bible ***does*** contain teachings that condemn homosexuality and other religions as sinful. If the WBC is 'cherry picking' by focusing on these hostile teachings and ignoring the loving ones, liberal Christians are also focusing on the loving teachings and ignoring the hostile ones. How can mainstream Christians justify doing this?

Key scholar **I. Howard Marshall** sets out to show how the Bible can be interpreted for today without falling into the extremes of fundamentalism (like the WBC) or liberalism (like Situation Ethics). **Frank J. Matera** also explores the unified voice of the Bible (he calls it the "*master story*") that puts its hostile teachings into a positive context.

KEY SCHOLARS

I. Howard Marshall

Topic: 6.2 How Should We Live?

I. Howard Marshall is a Scottish professor of theology. He is a Methodist (like **Morna Hooker**) but leans towards a conservative position. His area of specialism is **Luke's Gospel** and the **Book of Acts**. He is also a key scholar for **Topic: 5.1 The Kingdom of God in Luke** and **Topic 5.3 Crucifixion & Resurrection Narratives in Luke**.

Marshall is an evangelical Christian – he believes that the Bible should be taken literally as far as possible, he does not discount miracles and he thinks that, even though it is the product of many authors, it speaks with one voice in revealing God.

In **Beyond the Bible** (2004), Marshall explains that the task of Biblical interpretation is:

> *how we discover the message of the Bible for today, both for our fellow believers and for our non-Christian neighbours* – **I. Howard Marshall**

Marshall argues that the Gospel-writers and Paul were inspired but still could not *"foresee the world of which we are a part"* and therefore modern people have to interpret the Bible to work out how it should apply. Marshall points out that there are modern ethical problems where there is *"nothing closely analogous in Scripture"* and gives the examples of fertility treatment, genetic engineering and medical euthanasia.

Marshal argues for a balance between liberal and fundamentalist approaches: not ignoring parts of the Bible that contradict scientific understanding (e.g. the way **Rudolf Bultmann** does) but not rejecting scientific thinking either. Marshall talks about 'broadening horizons'. For example, the Old Testament often claims violence and genocide can solve moral problems, but in the New Testament that is a commandment to love your enemy. This broadens the ethical horizon and forces us to reinterpret the Old Testament rather than taking it at face value.

> *we do recognize that we are to listen to it in a different way from the original hearers* – **I. Howard Marshall**

Marshall applies this to the New Testament too. There are passages in the Gospels and in the Epistles that have a *"limited horizon"* because they represent 1st century values: slavery, women as second-class citizens and homosexuality as sinful are examples he considers.

> *we have to go beyond biblical teaching expressed in a specific cultural setting, for example in recognizing that slavery … is fundamentally at variance with the biblical understanding of man* – **I. Howard Marshall**

In going *beyond the Bible*, Marshall is prepared to admit the liberal argument that 'times have changed' but he still insists *"the Bible must be free to speak its prophetic and critical word to the practices and beliefs of our world."* He admits that this creates a *tension* that has no easy answer for Christians trying to work out an ethical response to issues like homosexuality.

Frank J. Matera

Topic 6.2 How Should We Live?

> *Is F. Matera the right scholar for this topic? Earlier versions of the Specification identify "L. Matera" but the recent editions confirm that Frank J. Matera is the intended scholar.*

Frank J. Matera is an American Catholic priest and professor of theology. Like **I. Howard Marshall**, he leans towards a conservative position but, as a Catholic, he feels free to interpret the Bible more liberally. He is also a key scholar for **Topic 5.3 Crucifixion & Resurrection Narratives in Luke**.

In *New Testament Ethics: The Legacies of Jesus & Paul* (1996), Matera acknowledges (rather like Marshall), that neither Jesus nor Paul left a complete ethical system behind, so modern readers have to interpret what they wrote and apply it to new situations that didn't exist in the 1st century. Matera distinguishes between **diachronic interpretation** (recognizing there are many authors in the New Testament and they all have different views) and **synchronic interpretation** (the idea that all these authors speak with one underlying voice – this is Marshall's position as well).

Matera resembles Marshall in that he tries to explore a 'middle way' between these approaches: he examines the teachings of each Gospel then harmonises them into a single ethical vision of how we should live today. For example, Matera looks at what is distinctive about Luke's Gospel:

> *The Gospel of Luke addresses a new situation in which Gentiles play a dominant role in the Church* – **Frank J. Matera**

Marshal argues this Gentile audience shapes Luke's ethical concerns, in which the **Law** and Jewish concepts of 'righteousness' become less important and there is more focus on universal ethical principles for ordinary people all over the Roman Empire. This can be seen in Luke's short **Sermon on the Plain** and the focus on social issues like poverty in his Parables.

However, as well as specific concerns, there is a unity to the New Testament:

> *The unity of New Testament theology is grounded in the implied master story ... Humanity finds itself in a predicament of its own making from which it cannot extricate itself* – **Frank J. Matera**

Matera argues that this *master-story* is timeless and therefore true today, even though our cultural situation has changed since the 1st century: we are still in a *predicament of our own making*, which includes our social inequality, sexual and ethnic conflicts and attitudes to money. Therefore, the Bible continues to offer us ethical advice.

Matera denies this ethical standard is too idealistic or impractical for modern people. He argues Christians must be '"*doers of the word rather than mere hearers,*" referring to **Luke 6: 46** where Jesus condemns those who call him '*Lord*' but "*do not do what I say.*"

GLOSSARY OF TERMS

Abraham: Ancestor of the Jewish race and founder of Judaism (lived perhaps 2000 BCE)

Acts: Fifth book of the New Testament describing the growth of the Christian religion guided by **Peter** and **Paul**; written by the same author as Luke's Gospel

Allegory: A text with a hidden or secondary meaning where the key features stand for something else

Apocalypticism: Belief in the coming end of the world

Apologetic: A text defending a religion; someone who defends their religion with arguments is an apologist

Ascension: Mysterious event when the Risen Jesus leaves this world and returns to his Heavenly Father

Atoning Death: A death that makes up for sins

Beatitude: Blessing; there are four blessings described in the **Sermon on the Plain**

Bosom of Abraham: 1st century Jewish belief in a paradise after death for the souls of righteous people

Cathar Heresy: Christian sect popular in the South of France in the Middle Ages; brutally suppressed by the Catholic Church and the Frankish nobility in the 12th-13th centuries

Celsus: Greek philosopher of the 2nd century CE who criticised Christianity

Cephas: Named used for **Peter** in **Paul**'s epistles (it is Aramaic for 'Rock', which is what 'Peter' means in Greek)

Cherry-picking: Selecting only details from a text that support a theory while ignoring those that don't

Christophany: Vision of the Risen Christ revealed to **Paul** on the road to Damascus

Conservatism: Christian trend opposed to **liberalism** and trying to conserve Biblical truths

Criterion of Embarrassment: Suggestion that a Biblical event may be historical since it contains details that go against early Christian beliefs

Dualism: Belief in **Hellenic** philosophy that there is a physical world and a (superior) spiritual world

Emmaus: Town where two disciples share a meal with the Risen Jesus; not identified and may be symbolic

Empty Tomb: Mystery of the tomb of Jesus being discovered with no body inside; reported in all the Gospels

Enlightenment, The: Period from mid 17th to late 18th century when European scholars pioneered a new scientific outlook

Eschatology: Beliefs about the end of the world and the afterlife

Eternal Life: Spiritually transformed life, either after death or in the present

Eucharist: Christian act of worship involving shared bread and wine representing Jesus' body and blood

Evangelical: A type of **conservative** Christianity that focuses on being 'Born Again' and interprets the Bible as literally as possible

Exclusivism: Belief that only your own religion is true and all other religions (and atheists) will go to Hell

Form Criticism: Interpretation of the Bible based on its origins as *pericopae* circulating among the first Christian communities

Galilee: Region to the north of **Judea** consisting of wooded hills and farmland surrounding Lake Galilee; an agricultural community with a mixture of Jews and **Gentiles**

Gentile: Someone who isn't Jewish by birth

Golden Rule: Moral code of reciprocity: treat others the way you want to be treated

Great Commission: Instruction by the Risen Jesus for his Disciples to go and spread his message to all people, including **Gentiles**

Great Commandment: Love God and love your neighbour as yourself

Hallucination Theory: Theory that the appearances of the Risen Jesus to his Disciples were hallucinations brought on by stress, grief or guilt

Hellenism: The Greek culture of the Roman Empire, especially its pagan religion, philosophy and art

Hypocrisy: Sin of pretending to be good but acting sinfully; someone guilty of this is a hypocrite

Johannine Community: Community of Jewish and Samaritan Christians who were expelled from the Synagogues, perhaps in Antioch c. 90 CE; composed John's Gospel

Joseph of Arimathea: Wealthy man who takes down Jesus' body and provides an empty and unused tomb for it to rest in

Judea: Province to the south of **Galilee** ruled by a Roman governor and centred on Jerusalem

Kingdom of God: rule of God over human life; may be a literal kingdom or a spiritual kingdom; may be experienced in the present or **eschatologically** (at the end of the world or after death)

Law: The religious rules of Judaism passed from God to Moses and written in the Torah; **Pharisees** believed in applying these rules to every aspect of life

Liberal Christianity: Christian trend opposed to **conservatism** and freely interpreting the Bible to fit new circumstances and modern knowledge

Luke-Acts: Luke's Gospel and Acts treated as a single book (since they have the same author)

Mary Magdalene: Female follower of Jesus; the first witness to the Resurrection in some Gospels

Moses: Greatest prophet and lawgiver in Judaism; received the **Law** from God (lived perhaps 1400 BCE)

Mythicist Hypothesis: Theory that pagan or Jewish myths were attributed to Jesus after his death, producing stories of a Resurrection believed to be real

Origen: Greek-Egyptian philosopher of the 3rd century CE who defended Christianity against **Celsus**

Parable: Story told by Jesus, usually with peasant characters but containing a spiritual message; there are several in the **Synoptic Gospels**, especially Luke

Parousia: The 'Second Coming' of Christ to judge the world

Paul: A Christian missionary who converted after persecuting the early Christians; previously known as Saul

Pericope: In **Form Criticism**, a textual unit that was originally a memory of Jesus passed on by word of mouth before the Gospels were written (plural *pericopae*)

Peter: The leader of the Twelve Disciples; also called Simon and **Cephas**

Pharisees: Jewish sect concerned with obeying the **Law** in every aspect of life

Pluralism: Arrangement where religions coexist and respect each other; also the belief that there is spiritual truth in all religions

Pontius Pilate: Roman *prefect* who governed **Judea** and sentenced Jesus to death

Prophecy: A statement (often in the form of poetry) that reveals the will of God to humans

Q-Source: Theoretical source for material common to Matthew and Luke that is not shared by Mark

Redaction Criticism: Interpretation of the Bible based on the idea of a redactor editing earlier material to address issues going on in the church in his time

Repentance: Feeling guilty for your sins and resolving to make amends to God; first stage of **atonement**

Sabbath: The 7th day of the week; Jewish Sabbath regulations forbid many types of work

Samaria: Hilly region between **Galilee** and **Judea**; homeland of the **Samaritans**

Samaritan: A religious group hated by 1st century Jews because of their different traditions about how to worship God

Sermon on the Plain: Sermon delivered by Jesus in Luke's Gospel, featuring teachings about loving your enemy and not judging each other

Sheol: Hebrew for 'the Grave'; word used for the Afterlife in the Old Testament; translated as *Hades* in New Testament Greek

Son of Man: Title Jesus adopted for himself based on prophecies in the Old Testament

Swoon Theory: The idea that Jesus did not die on the cross and instead recovered later in the tomb

Synoptic Gospel: Matthew, Mark and Luke; from the Greek 'seen together' because of the shared content and structure of these Gospels

Theft Hypothesis: Theory that Jesus' body was stolen from the tomb (by his Disciples or by the Jewish authorities)

Woe: A curse or warning; thee are four Woes described in the **Sermon on the Plain**

Vision Theory: The theory that the appearances of the Risen Jesus were visions sent by God rather than a bodily resurrection

TOPIC 6 IN THE EXAM

A-Level Paper 3 (New Testament)

Section A

1   Explore the idea of the Resurrection as myth. (8 marks)

"Explore" questions award marks for AO1 (knowledge & understanding). You don't need to evaluate any of these conflicts – just describe them. This question is pretty specific but it could focus on "fictional event" or "event in the experience of the disciples" instead.

2   Assess the significance of the work of Frank Morison for understanding the Resurrection. (12 marks)

"Assess" questions award some marks for AO1 (4 marks in this question) but more for AO2 (evaluation – 8 marks in this question). You need to describe a bit about the content of this topic (such as Morison's view of the Theft hypothesis), but more about how it should be interpreted (are Morison's arguments convincing?).

Section B

The Rich Man and Lazarus

[19] "There was a rich man who was dressed in purple and fine linen and lived in luxury every day. [20] At his gate was laid a beggar named Lazarus, covered with sores [21] and longing to eat what fell from the rich man's table. Even the dogs came and licked his sores.

[22] "The time came when the beggar died and the angels carried him to Abraham's side. The rich man also died and was buried. [23] In Hades, where he was in torment, he looked up and saw Abraham far away, with Lazarus by his side. [24] So he called to him, 'Father Abraham, have pity on me and send Lazarus to dip the tip of his finger in water and cool my tongue, because I am in agony in this fire.'

[25] "But Abraham replied, 'Son, remember that in your lifetime you received your good things, while Lazarus received bad things, but now he is comforted here and you are in agony. [26] And besides all this, between us and you a great chasm has been set in place, so that those who want to go from here to you cannot, nor can anyone cross over from there to us.'

[27] "He answered, 'Then I beg you, father, send Lazarus to my family, [28] for I have five brothers. Let him warn them, so that they will not also come to this place of torment.'

[29] "Abraham replied, 'They have Moses and the Prophets; let them listen to them.'

³⁰ "'No, father Abraham,' he said, 'but if someone from the dead goes to them, they will repent.'

³¹ "He said to him, 'If they do not listen to Moses and the Prophets, they will not be convinced even if someone rises from the dead.'"

Quote from New International Translation, Luke 16: 19-31

3   (a) Clarify the ideas illustrated in this passage about the ethical teaching of Jesus. *You must refer to the passage in your response.* (10 marks)

"Clarify" questions only award marks for AO1 (knowledge & understanding), so all that is required is description. There is no need to evaluate whether this is a Parable or not – just discuss the ethical message about poverty, wealth, death and the Jewish prophets.

(b) Analyse the claim that Jesus' ethical teachings are impractical. (20 marks)

This "Analyse" question awards some marks for AO1 (5 marks in this question), but mostly for AO2 (15 marks in this question). You need to describe a bit about the content (such as forgiving enemies and loving neighbours), but more about whether it is practical or not (are these teaching idealistic? how do we run into problems if we try to live by them?).

Section C

4   "If there was no Resurrection, Christianity is simply false."

Evaluate this view. In your response to this question, you must include how developments in New Testament Studies have been influenced by one of the following:

* Philosophy of Religion
* Religion and Ethics
* the study of a religion (other than Christianity)   (30 marks)

This "Evaluate" question awards some marks for AO1 (5 marks in this question), but mostly for AO2 (25 marks). You need to describe a bit about the content (such as challenges to the Resurrection), but more about whether this discredits the rest of Christianity (e.g. ethical teachings, liberal interpretations). In order to attain beyond the top of level 4 (i.e. score 25+) you must link to another area of the course (such as religious experience or religion & morality).

Total = 90 marks

In these examples, all the questions are drawn from Topic 6. A real A-Level exam would draw from Topics 1-5 as well.

LOOKING BACK OVER YEAR 2...

If you are studying for the A-Level exam, you have reached the end of the New Testament Studies course. When revising this course, it is helpful to 'work backwards'.

Start off by reflecting on the link between the **Resurrection** and **Jesus' ethical teaching**. This raises the question, *What IS Christianity?* Is it a belief in a world-changing supernatural event that happened on Easter morning 2000 years ago – and perhaps a world-ending Apocalypse that could occur in the imminent future? Or is it a set of moral teachings to love and forgive and be generous? Can you stop believing in the Resurrection as a physical event in history and still be a Christian? Or is believing in the Resurrection part of the life-changing transformation (called being 'Born Again' in **John's Gospel**) that goes beyond just following moral rules?

- Are Christians moral people following the wise teachings of a man who died 2000 years ago?
- Or are they people who have been transformed by their faith in Christ who still lives and guides them?

Reflecting on this will help you decide whether the **Kingdom of God** in **Topic 5** is supposed to be an event in future history, a spiritual change that comes over people today or a description of the Afterlife.

- Did Jesus teach a spiritual message of transformation and love that was misunderstood by his literal-minded followers?
- Or did Jesus predict a literal Apocalypse that never occurred – with his later followers salvaging a message of love and goodness from the failure of his 'Kingdom' to materialise?

This will help you look again at Jesus' **conflicts with authority**, his **trial** and **crucifixion** in **Topic 5**.

- Was Jesus trying to tell people something they were too blind or bigoted to hear? If so, his message might still be relevant today, even though the people of his own time misunderstood him.
- Or was he an innocent pawn caught up in the political intrigue of the Jewish priests and the Roman Empire? If so, he's a tragic loser and later Christians misunderstood him.

This theme of 'misunderstanding' runs through our analysis of the Gospels. **John's Gospel** frequently represents people misunderstanding Jesus, but a lot of Biblical criticism suggests that it may be the later Christians who have misunderstood things – and that the historical Jesus might have been nothing like the 'Christ of faith'.

With this is mind you can look again at the conflict between **Barth** and **Bultmann** in **Topic 4**. Bultmann assumes Jesus and his message have been massively misunderstood by Christians and atheists. He wants to 'wipe the slate clean' and look at Jesus again with fresh eyes so we can all take a new message from the Gospels. Barth thinks any attempt to interpret the Bible with philosophy will only lead to misunderstanding. He thinks that the Bible is our only witness to the Word of God in Jesus – and we have to read it as if it's speaking to us personally.

ABOUT THE AUTHOR

Jonathan Rowe is a teacher of Religious Studies, Psychology and Sociology at Spalding Grammar School and he creates and maintains **www.philosophydungeon.weebly.com** and the **www.psychologywizard.net** site for Edexcel A-Level Psychology. He has worked as an examiner for various Exam Boards but is not affiliated with Edexcel. This series of books grew out of the resources he created for his students. Jonathan also writes novels and creates resources for his hobby of fantasy wargaming. He likes warm beer and smooth jazz.

24216508R00054

Printed in Great Britain
by Amazon